Hand on Heart

ISBN 0-9543247-8-1

First published September 2004

Distributed and published by
**ENDpapers, P.O. Box 69, YORK, YO1 7WZ
ENGLAND**
Tel: **+44 (0)1904 610676**
Fax: **+44 (0)1904 643049**
Email: **info@endpapers.co.uk**
www.endpapers.co.uk

Printed by **Fratelli Spada, Rome.**

HAND ON HEART
a perfectly ordinary cookbook

Dr. Tim Harlan

TEXT LAYOUT & DESIGN
Ian Forster & Vince Danks

ILLUSTRATIONS
Rachel Stainsby

INTRODUCTION

Food is life.

The writers who have contributed to the HAND series have understood this so well, with Hand to Mouth relishing cooks and their recipes, and Hand in Hand rejoicing in children and the ties between food and life. Hand on Heart was written to continue this celebration of our connection to food.

This book is about the foods that you can eat. Eating healthily is about eating great food, the food you like and know, as well as those you should know.

The key is balance. No single change – whether it is it low carb, reduced fat, high protein, low salt, etc. – will be satisfying for the long haul. Balance will. By exploring a variety of foods, and learning techniques to maximize flavours and textures whilst reducing calories, fat and salt, you can eat healthy and wonderful food.

The recipes have been chosen to illustrate these techniques, equipment and ingredients, placing them in the context of the current medical research about how what we eat affects our health. At the front of the book are ideas for creating a new pantry, as well as equipment that will make cooking healthier recipes a breeze.

So many people deserve my thanks for their help. At the top of the list is Magdelena Chávez and the amazing folks at ENDpapers, as well as my brilliant parents Katherine and Bill Harlan. I am grateful for the help of John Hebden, Sue Pritchett and Nancy Hull, the Smith Family (especially Frank & BJ), the Windrow-Klein household, the Pearsons, Lesley Franken, Denice Hardman and, of course, Mrs. Cecilia Hatfield. None of this would have been possible without my brother Bruce who is responsible for the very existence of Dr. Gourmet. And most importantly, my muse, Morgan Ladd.

This book is for my brother Chris who continues to touch my life every day.

Dr. Tim Harlan

THE HAND SERIES

It is with great pleasure that we **add** Hand on Heart – *a perfectly ordinary cookbook* to the HAND series.

Making the cooking and eating habits Dr. Tim is suggesting an ordinary part of our daily lives is the great attraction of his book for the HAND series.

By that I mean the recipes are simple, recognisable, yet with great taste appeal. Furthermore they are within the gift of most cooks, from the least confident to the most experienced. Moreover, there is no need for a large budget or a professionally equipped kitchen to reproduce Dr. Tim's recipes successfully. As a result it is easy to make the preparation of the recipes in Hand on Heart a perfectly ordinary part of life. Consequently we can have a greater chance of living longer and better.

With exhaustive nutritional information, clear guidance on techniques and equipment, Dr. Tim Harlan's Hand on Heart – *a perfectly ordinary cookbook* takes the HAND series forward.

At the same time he has maintained what is common to each of the titles in that it is stuffed with accessible recipes for quality food that is a joy to eat and to share.

Magdalena Chávez
Originator of the HAND series

CONTENTS

Each recipe shows nutritional information per serving and its percentage of recommended daily intake.

 Quick and Easy are recipes that will take about a half an hour or slightly more.

 Vegetarian recipes do not contain meat or gelatine. Most wines nowadays use vegetarian production methods.

 Vegan recipes are vegetarian and additionally do not contain honey, yeast, eggs or dairy products. Wine processing should be checked for recipes including wine.

 Gluten-free meals are free of gluten and indicate where to check for ingredients in proprietary brands.

 Special Occasion Meals are those that might take a little longer but are worth the effort. Often there will be leftovers.

 Healthy Pantry recipes are those that use some of the ingredients from the Healthy Pantry and Starter Kit sections. For instance, if you have yeast and tomato sauce on hand, you are half-way to a great pizza. A few veggies or leftovers from the fridge complete the recipe.

 Low or no sugar meals are those that are lower in concentrated sugars. This doesn't mean that as a diabetic you have to stay away from the others – just be aware of the added sugar.

Soups

	RECIPE	Q	V	V+	G	S	H	N
Black Bean	3				✔			✔
Corn Chowder	6				✔			✔
Mulligatawny	4				✔	✔		✔
Potato and Leek	5	✔	✔		✔			✔
Roasted Aubergine	1		✔	Check Wine	✔			✔
Shrimp Gazpacho	7	✔			✔			✔
Spring Bisque	2	✔	✔	✔	✔			✔

Salads

	RECIPE	Q	V	V+	G	S	H	N
Caesar Salad	13	✔						✔
Curried Chicken	8	✔			Check Chutney & Mayo			✔
Red Potato	9	✔	✔		Check Mayo			✔
Thai Cucumber	12	✔	✔	✔	✔		✔	✔
Tomato Chive	11	✔	✔	Check Wine	✔		✔	✔
Vinaigrette Potato	10	✔	✔	Check Wine	✔			✔

RECIPE		Q	V	V+	G	S	H	N
Apple Pancake	18		✔			✔		
Barbeque Chicken	21				Check Sauces		✔	
Basil Pesto	20	✔	Check Rennet		✔			✔
Beef Stew	31				Check Sauces	✔		✔
Carribean Shrimp	36	✔			✔			✔
Coconut Rice	52	✔	✔	✔	✔			✔
Cornbread Muffins	24	✔	✔		✔			
Courgette & Chévre Frittatta	16	✔	Check Rennet		✔			✔
Dill Pesto	41	✔	Check Rennet		✔			✔
Eggs Benedict	14		✔		✔	✔		✔
Fettuccine Alfredo	19	✔	Check Rennet				✔	✔
Fillet Steak with Roasted Pepper & Blue Cheese Sauce	30	✔			✔			✔
French Fries	22		✔	✔	✔		✔	✔
Ginger Coriander Flank Steak	32				✔	✔		✔
Grilled Lamb Kebabs	35				✔	✔		✔
Hollandaise Sauce	15		✔		✔	✔	✔	✔
Jerk Rub	37	✔	✔	✔	✔			✔
Lemon Butter Brussels Sprouts	27	✔	✔		✔			
Lemon Pork Chops with Lentils	34	✔			✔			✔

Savouries

RECIPE		Q	V	V+	G	S	H	N
London Broil with Mushrooms Sauteéd in Cognac	28				✔	✔		✔
Mango or Melon Salsa	38	✔	✔	✔	✔			
Maple Herb Crusted Rib Eye Steak	29	✔			✔		✔	
Mussels in White Wine and Herbed Butter	43	✔			✔		✔	✔
Oven Fried Chicken	23					✔	✔	✔
Pizza Dough	39		✔				✔	✔
Pizza with Dill pesto and Potato	40		Check Rennet					✔
Pizza with Tomato, Basil and Garlic	42		Check Rennet					✔
Roasted Garlic	26	✔	✔	✔	✔		✔	✔
Roasted Garlic Mashed Potatoes	25	✔	✔		✔		✔	✔
Roasted Salmon and Corn Relish	48				✔			✔
Roasted Salmon with Caper Mayonaise	47	✔			Check Mayo		✔	✔
Salmon with Parmesan Crust	49	✔						✔
Scallops with White Wine & Herbed Butter	44	✔			✔		✔	✔
Seared Halibut with Basil Pea Pureé	46	✔			✔			✔

Q	V	V+	G	S	H	N
Quick and Easy	Vegetarian	Vegan	Gluten Free	Special Occasion	Healthy Pantry	Low or No Sugar

Each recipe shows nutritional information per serving and its percentage of recommended daily intake.

Savouries

RECIPE		Q	V	V+	G	S	H	N
Seared Tuna with Sake-Wasabi Sauce	50	✔			Use Tamari			✔
Shiitake & Cranberry Stuffed Pork Loin	33				✔	✔		
Soy Mustard Scallops	45	✔			Use Tamari		✔	✔
Thai Coconut Shrimp	51	✔			Check Sauces	✔		✔
Tortilla	17	✔	✔		✔			✔
Yellow Pepper & White Asparagus Soft Tacos	53		✔					✔

Sweets

RECIPE		Q	V	V+	G	S	H	N
Banoffee Pie	57		✔			✔		
Cheesecake	54		✔			✔		✔
Chocolate Sauce	55	✔	✔		✔			
Chocolate Soufflé	56	✔	✔		✔	✔		
Crème Brûlée	60		✔		✔		✔	✔
Custard Cream	58	✔	✔				✔	✔
Poached Pears	59		✔		✔		✔	✔
Whipped Cream	61				✔		✔	✔

Equipment Starter Kit

Here are a few kitchen utensils that are helpful when cooking healthy food. Some of these are to make the job easier and others help reduce the amount of fat or calories in a recipe. You don't have to go out and buy all of these before you start but add them as you increase your skills. I have listed them in order of priority.

Non-stick pans
These are among the most important pieces of equipment that you can buy. They help with so many recipes by allowing reduction of the amount of fat needed to cook foods. See recipe 45, Soy Mustard Scallops, for more detailed information.

Knives
Chef's knife – about 10–12 inches long, with a curved blade that allows easier slicing by rocking from the tip to the hilt. Great for just about everything, from cutting meat and fish to mincing parsley.
Paring knife – about 6–8 inches long with a thin tapered blade for filleting fish and cutting up vegetables.
A long serrated knife – works well for carving cooked meats as well as slicing bread.
A knife sharpener – get whatever you can afford but ask the kitchen shop for help on how to use it. A sharp knife will give you more control over the foods you are working on, and consequently there will be less risk of cutting yourself.

Oil spray can
This ranks just behind the non-stick pan because being able to spray just a bit of oil for searing foods, or in baking, saves a ton of fat and calories. See recipe 16, Courgette and Chévre Frittata, for more information.

Measuring cups and spoons and a scale that weighs in ounces and grams
Measuring is the key to not getting more oil, butter, maple syrup or other high calorie ingredients. See Recipe 38, Mango or Melon Salsa, for more information.

Stock pot
A 10–12 litre pot is excellent for making soups and stews. Try and find one with two inserts. One is a deep perforated liner for making and draining pasta and the other is a shallow one, suitable for steaming vegetables.

Steamer basket
Even if you buy a stockpot that doubles as a steamer, having a small steamer basket makes cooking so convenient. A small collapsible steamer basket that will fit in a saucepan is so inexpensive it's worth considering getting two.

Roasting pan
You don't have to spend a lot of money on a roasting pan. Do buy one that is large enough (at least 17in x 13in x 5½ in/43cm x 33cm x 14cm). This is not just for roasting a large turkey, but also for roasting vegetables, potatoes and such like. It's important to use a pan large enough so the ingredients don't touch. When they do, they steam and end up mushy instead of having a brown and crispy crust.

Stick blender
Quite simply, the best money you will spend on any kitchen appliance. See Recipe 2, Spring Bisque, for more information.

Non-reactive pan
Having a 2–4 litre pan made of stainless steel or clad with porcelain is a good idea because sauces that are more acidic will often react with a porous pan, such as one made from aluminium or cast iron.

Tongs
I have a pair of what are called "clamshell" tongs. These are stainless steel, about 12 inches long, spring-loaded and have broad tips that are perfect for everything from picking up vegetables to grabbing the top off a stock pot.

Mandoline
This is not an essential item but it can make slicing chores so much easier. See Recipe 12, Thai Cucumber Salad, for more information.

Ziplock bags
These are a luxury item, but having a plastic bag that seals tightly, makes storing items, like marinating foods, so easy.

Pizza stone
I love pizza and make it often. You should too – it can be a wonderfully healthy meal. A pizza stone will make your pizza turn out like a pro. See Recipe 40, Pizza with Dill Pesto and Potato, for more information.

The Healthy Pantry

These ingredients don't need to be purchased all at once but as you shop, consider picking up one or two on each trip to the market to complete your pantry.

Spray oil
I prefer to use my own spray can (see Equipment Starter Kit) but there are now plenty of canned oils on the market shelves.

Prepared chicken stock
Look for a non-fat/low-sodium stock. These recipes are based on a store-bought stock that has 30 calories, 380mg sodium and 0g fat per cup.

Fresh herbs
This is one of the most important ingredients in cooking and fresh herbs enrich any recipe. You can grow your own during the season or buy them as you need.

Shallots
As with fresh herbs, shallots will make almost any savoury recipe better.

Oils
I keep extra virgin olive oil, rapeseed oil, dark sesame oil and grapeseed oil in my pantry at all times.

Vinegars
I use Rice Vinegar in Asian recipes but also in those where I want lower acidity. Having Red Wine Vinegar and Balsamic Vinegar in your pantry will have you ready for almost any dressing or marinade.

Melba toast
The perfect low-fat breading.

Prepared sauces
Sauces in the book, like Wasabi Paste and Red Bean Paste, are just the beginning. Having tomato paste, different mustards or a spicy Harissa in your pantry will have you prepared for great recipes. Pick up a new interesting sauce each time you go to the market. Look for ones with less than 5g of fat in 2Tbl and as few calories as possible.

Unsalted butter
Keep your butter sealed tightly in a container so it won't pick up flavours from the fridge.

Cheeses
If the cheese is full-fat like Stilton or Parmigiano-Reggiano Parmesan, look for the best quality you can find because you need less. Keep low-fat cheeses, like many goat cheeses and Mozzarella as well as low-fat Swiss and cheddar cheeses, on hand.

Pure maple syrup
This lovely ingredient can add the "mouthfeel" of oil to a recipe but with less fat and calories.

Cornflour
An essential thickening agent. See Hollandaise Sauce – Recipe 15 for more information.

Splenda
This is a great substitute for sugar in almost all applications.

Buttermilk
Buttermilk enriches sauces, dressings and baking. See Roasted Garlic Mashed Potatoes – Recipe 25 for more information.

Tomato sauce
There are great non-fat sauces on the market but look for ones with less than 5g of fat in a cup.

Pasta
Keep some penne or fettuccine in your panty and you will always have a healthy meal. You can pair it with leftover pesto or other sauces like that good quality tomato sauce in the back of the pantry. Remember that a serving is 2oz/57g.

Active Dry Yeast
If you have yeast on hand you can easily combine it with flour, and great freshly made pizza is only 90 minutes away.

Other items
These items are ones that are found in a lot of healthy recipes and having them on hand helps you pull off almost any recipe

Low-fat mayonnaise
Low-fat sour cream
Fresh lemons & limes
Low-sodium soy sauce
Low-sodium Worcestershire sauce
Low-sodium ketchup

Memories are like mulligatawny soup in a cheap restaurant. It is best not to stir them

P.G. Wodehouse
Novelist

soups

Roasted Aubergine Soup

Calories 161
Calories from Fat 18
Total Fat 1g (2%)
Saturated Fat 0g (0%)
Cholesterol 0mg (0%)
Sodium 184mg (8%)
Total Carbohydrates 23g (8%)
Dietary Fibre 6g (24%)
Protein 10g
Vitamin A (1%)
Vitamin C (3%)
Calcium (7%)
Iron (11%)

Dr. Tim says...

This is, quite simply, my favourite soup. It is simple, elegant and so good for you.

¼lb/113g aubergine = 29 calories, 0g fat, 0g sat fat, 0g mono fat, 1g protein, 7g carbohydrates, 4mg sodium, 0mg cholesterol, 3g fibre

It is simple, elegant and so good for you.

Chef Tim says...

Aubergines have a very short shelf life so it is best to buy them on the day of use. They turn bitter quickly even when they are not overripe. Some of the bitterness can be removed by slicing them and liberally sprinkling the cut edges with salt. After about 20 minutes rinse well to remove all the salt.

An aubergine is ripe when pressed, gives slightly, but springs back into shape. Look for one with a smooth unblemished skin. Darkening and/or brown spots indicate bruising. If it remains dented where pressed, it is overripe – don't buy it.

Serves 6
Serving size = about 2 cups
Keeps well for 3–4 days refrigerated
Easily multiplied by 2

½ lb/225g plum tomatoes (halved)
1½ lbs/700g large aubergine (quartered lengthwise)
½ lb/225g shallots (peeled and halved)
6 large garlic cloves (peeled)
olive oil spray
1 tsp dried thyme
½ cup white wine
2 cups water
4 cups chicken stock
¼ tsp salt
1 cup semi-skimmed milk

Preheat oven to 400°F/205°C. Place vegetables in a large roasting pan. Spray lightly with olive oil. Roast for about 45 minutes or until tender and brown in spots.

Remove from oven. When cool, scoop aubergine from skin into medium pan. Discard skin. Add other roasted vegetables, thyme, white wine and water and place over a medium-high heat. Add chicken stock and bring to boil. Reduce heat to medium-low and simmer for 45 minutes or until vegetables are tender. Cool slightly. Blend with a stick blender until smooth. Stir in milk and salt. Reheat gently.

Spring Bisque

Calories 103
Calories from Fat 18
Total Fat 2g (3%)
Saturated Fat 1g (5%)
Cholesterol 5mg (2%)
Sodium 200mg (8%)
Total Carbohydrates 16g (5%)
Dietary Fibre 2g (8%)
Protein 4g
Vitamin A (324%)
Vitamin C (47%)
Calcium (12%)
Iron (5%)

Dr. Tim says...

Another very simple and lovely soup that is so good for you. With a nice hunk of brown bread spread with an ounce of goat cheese you have the perfect meal.

Just because bread is labelled "Wheat Bread" doesn't mean it's a more nutritious loaf. Wheat bread is simply made with wheat flour and this could be enriched all-purpose white flour. For a bread that is made from the whole wheatberry look for a label that says "Whole Wheat" or "100% Whole Wheat". Some breads are made with a combination of white and whole wheat flour and the ingredient list will indicate both.

Chef Tim says...

When using a stick blender wait for hot recipes to cool a bit before blending. Place the bottom of the blender against the bottom of the pot or bowl. This actually forms a slight suction and foods will tend to spatter less.

Serves 8
Serving size = about 2 cups
Keeps well for 3–4 days in the refrigerator
Serve hot or cold
Easily multiplied by 2

1 tsp extra virgin olive oil
2 medium white onions (peeled and diced)
2lbs/900g yellow squash (chopped into 1 inch cubes)
1lb/450g carrots (peeled and shredded)
½ cup white wine
1 litre water
1 tsp dried marjoram
½ tsp salt
2 cups semi-skimmed milk

In a large non-stick frying pan over medium heat cook onions in olive oil until translucent. Stir frequently and do not allow to brown. Add squash, carrots and wine and cook for about 5 minutes, stirring frequently. Add the water. Increase heat to high. Boil for about 2 minutes. Reduce heat to low and simmer. When the carrots are tender, about 25 to 30 minutes, turn off the heat. Cool for about 15 minutes. Add the marjoram and salt. Blend until smooth. Add milk, blend again, and serve.

Another very simple and lovely soup

3

Black Bean Soup

Calories 150
Calories from Fat 18
Total Fat 2g (3%)
Saturated Fat 0g (0%)
Cholesterol 0mg (0%)
Sodium 200mg (8%)
Total Carbohydrates 20g (7%)
Dietary Fibre 2g (8%)
Protein 9g
Vitamin A (1%)
Vitamin C (40%)
Calcium (20%)
Iron (13%)

Dr. Tim says...

Tinned vegetables almost always have salt in them. Check the label carefully. Depending on the vegetable, it is usually better to buy frozen vegetables because they seldom have added salt. Most are frozen right at the field where they are picked. Because of being frozen so soon after being picked many actually have more nutrients than fresh vegetables. Rinsing tinned veggies like these beans will remove some, but not all, of the salt.

whenever possible use fresh herbs

Chef Tim says...

How long have the spices, that you have, been in your cupboard? Too long probably. Most will last about 6 months and then lose most of their flavour. Try to buy small amounts, use fresh herbs wherever possible and grind spices, like cumin, from the seeds.

Serves 8
Serving size = 1 cup
Leftovers keep for about 48 hours in the refrigerator
Easily multiplied by 2

2 tsp olive oil
1 cup white onion (diced)
2 cloves garlic (peeled and diced)
3 leeks (cleaned well and chopped)
½ cup celery (diced)
2 bay leaves
4 cups chicken stock
12 peppercorns
½ cup sherry
2 x 19oz/525g tins black beans (rinsed and drained)

Heat oil in a large pan over medium heat adding onions, garlic, leeks and celery. Stir until onions are translucent. Add bay leaves, chicken stock, peppercorns, sherry and black beans. Reduce to low heat for about one hour until the beans are very soft. Remove ⅓ cup of beans. Blend remaining soup until smooth. Add the reserved beans to smooth soup, then serve.

Mulligatawny

Calories 119
Calories from Fat 9
Total Fat 1g (2%)
Saturated Fat <1g (0%)
Cholesterol 12mg (4%)
Sodium 577mg (24%)
Total Carbohydrates 16g (5%)
Dietary Fibre 2g (8%)
Protein 8g
Vitamin A (27%)
Vitamin C (26%)
Calcium 2%
Iron 5%

Dr. Tim says...

This is one of those soups that is pretty much a meal in itself. It has everything that you would want in a meal – a protein, veggies, starch, and even a fruit.

There is very good research about the residents of Okinawa who appear to have the longest life expectancy of any culture in the world. The staple of their diet is a soup of (usually) chicken broth with noodles and a small amount of meat or seafood.

¼lb/113g tomato = 24 calories, 0g fat, 0g sat fat, 0g mono fat, 1g protein, 5g carbohydrates, 10mg sodium, 0mg cholesterol

"Memories are like mulligatawny soup in a cheap restaurant. It is best not to stir them."

P. G. Wodehouse
novelist

Chef Tim says...

Curry powder is the yellow powder you usually buy in the supermarket, but there are infinite variations of curry powder. In the Far East they vary by individual cook, region, country, even the class of who is being served. Most curries are spicier than the yellow curry that you may be used to.

Originally curry powders were shipped back to Europe when the East India Company controlled much of the spice traffic. At first these varied greatly in their tastes, colour and spiciness. At the Universal Paris Exhibition of 1889 a standardised curry powder was agreed upon and most recipes are subtle variations of that formula.

It is the turmeric that gives curry its yellow colour and other ingredients include onion, pepper, ground cumin, ground coriander, tamarind, chilli powder, fenugreek and mustard powder.

Serves 8
Serving size = 1½ cups
Keeps well for 4–5 days refrigerated and is better the second day
Easily multiplied by 2

1 cup water
½ cup brown rice
1 litre chicken stock
¼ cup onion (diced)
¼ cup celery (diced)
¼ cup carrots (diced)
¼ cup green pepper (diced)
2 tsp curry powder
1lb/450g fresh tomatoes (quartered, seeded & cut into ¼ inch strips)
½ lb/225g cooked turkey breast (cubed)
1 apple (cubed)

Boil water in a medium pan. Add the brown rice and stir once. Cover and reduce the heat to a simmer. Cook until all of the water is gone. Do not stir the rice. Remove from heat.

Place the onions, celery, carrots, pepper and chicken stock in a large pan. Cook over low heat until the onions begin to soften. Add the curry powder and the cooked rice to the soup. Add the tomatoes, turkey and apples to the soup. Cook over low heat until the apples are just tender, then serve.

"It has everything that you would want in a meal"

5

Potato and Leek Soup

Calories 156

Calories from Fat 36

Total Fat 4g (6%)

Saturated Fat 2g (8%)

Cholesterol 15mg (5%)

Sodium 271mg (11%)

Total Carbohydrates 23g (8%)

Dietary Fibre 2g (8%)

Protein 8g

Vitamin A (10%)

Vitamin C (23%)

Calcium (29%)

Iron (11%)

Dr. Tim says...

Does cooking reduce nutrients in foods? The simple answer is yes but not by much. High heat can cause some vitamins to breakdown. It's the way foods are cooked, however, that affects the amount of vitamins in a finished recipe. Simmering carrots in a beef stew results in a greater loss of these vitamins than when they are quickly sautéed. Most other nutrients like fats, minerals and fibre are not changed significantly by cooking, and many are made more digestible with cooking (as with proteins in meats or fibre in cooked oats).

Much more important is the freshness of food. 'Fresh' fruits and veggies are sometimes a week or more old before they make it into our refrigerators. In one study published in the Journal of Agricultural and Food Chemistry, it was shown that many of the cancer preventing nutrients (known as phytochemicals) were lost as vegetables aged under conditions similar to those in supermarkets and refrigerators. Interestingly, tinned or frozen vegetables are usually more nutritious because they are preserved soon after being picked.

¼lb/113g leek = 69 calories, 0g fat, 0g sat fat, 0g mono fat, 2g protein, 16g carbohydrates, 23mg sodium, 0mg cholesterol

Much more important is the freshness of food

Chef Tim says...

The white part of leeks grows below ground, so they are often dirty. Cut the leek at the lower end of the green top and run water over the leaves as they separate. Usually the rings of the white part have dirt embedded in them towards the top. Slice the leek in an X across the top and gently clean the dirt from between the rings under cold water.

Serves 8
Serving size = about 2 cups
Keeps well for 4–5 days refrigerated and is better the second day
Easily multiplied by 2

½ Tbl unsalted butter
1 large white onion (peeled and diced)
2 ribs celery (chopped)
3 medium russet potatoes (peeled and chopped)
3 large leeks (cleaned and sliced thinly)
3 cups water
3 cups semi-skimmed milk
½ tsp salt
½ tsp pepper

Melt the butter in a large non-stick frying pan over a medium heat and add the onions. Cook, stirring frequently until slightly soft and translucent. Add the celery and cook for about 2 minutes more. Add the leeks and cook until they are limp, stirring frequently. Reduce heat to medium-low and add the potatoes and water. Cook for 20–25 minutes until the potatoes are slightly soft. Add water, as needed, to keep the potato and leek mixture covered. When the potatoes are soft, add the milk slowly, stirring continuously. Add the salt and pepper. Gently reheat the soup, then serve.

Corn Chowder

Calories 316

Calories from Fat 56

Total Fat 8g (12%)

Saturated Fat 4g (20%)

Cholesterol 21mg (7%)

Sodium 360mg (15%)

Total Carbohydrates 54g (18%)

Dietary Fibre 5g (20%)

Protein 12g

Vitamin A (13%)

Vitamin C (67%)

Calcium (18%)

Iron (10%)

Dr. Tim says...

In a study performed in 1982, an experimental group of people were placed on a low sodium diet for 5 months. Their taste responses to salt in solutions, soups and crackers were measured before and during the diet. The same measurements were made in a control group.

In the experimental group the perceived intensity of salt in crackers increased while the amount of salt needed for "maximum pleasantness" of taste in soup and crackers fell. In the control group nothing changed.

It is clear that preferred levels of salt in food are dependent on how much salt you are used to eating. So, give it some time and slowly decrease the amount of salt in foods you prepare and your perceptions of saltiness will change.

Chef Tim says...

Thickening sauces and soups can be accomplished by a variety of agents but most rely on a starch. Even though starches like flour and potatoes are mostly carbohydrates, they also have proteins that, when heated, interact with liquid to thicken them. Most cream soups have a milk or cream base, but with chowder it is primarily the potatoes that act as the thickening agent.

Serves 6
Serving Size = 1½ cups
Keeps well for 48–72 hours
Easily multiplied by 2

2 Tbl unsalted butter
2 cups white onion (finely chopped)
4 cloves garlic (finely chopped)
2lbs/900g russet potatoes (peeled)
4 ears (3 cups) corn kernels
2 cups chicken stock
3 cups semi-skimmed milk
1 tsp fresh thyme leaves
¼ tsp salt
⅛ tsp pepper

On medium heat melt the butter in a medium pan. Add the garlic and onion to the butter and cook gently but do not allow them to turn brown. When the onions are translucent and slightly soft, add the potatoes, corn, chicken stock and milk. Cook on a very low heat for about an hour. Do not allow the soup to boil. Add the fresh thyme, salt and pepper and cook for 15 minutes more. Remove. Cool and then chill, at least overnight. Reheat soup very gently for about 20 minutes before serving.

with chowder it is primarily the potatoes that act as the thickening agent

Shrimp Gazpacho

Calories 163
Calories from Fat 18
Total Fat 2g (3%)
Saturated Fat 0g (0%)
Cholesterol 115mg (38%)
Sodium 345mg (14%)
Total Carbohydrates 20g (7%)
Dietary Fibre 4g (6%)
Protein 19g
Vitamin A (47%)
Vitamin C (126%)
Calcium (8%)
Iron (23%)

Dr. Tim says...

Lycopenes are the red pigments found in many fruits and vegetables. In a recent study of this antioxidant in over 45,000 men at Harvard University, researchers found that eating foods high in lycopene reduced the risk of prostate cancer by about 35%. Studies also show lycopenes have a beneficial effect on bad cholesterol. Tomatoes are one of the best sources of lycopenes and cooking them helps release the antioxidant. Other red pigment fruits and vegetables, like watermelon and grapefruit, are also good sources.

shrimp

Chef Tim says...

The one ingredient that helps distinguish a good dish from a great one is fresh herbs. Certainly the best and least expensive way is to plant herbs but, of course, this limits availability. Most groceries have a fair choice of fresh herbs and specialty stores will carry even more.

The rule of thumb when there is no choice but dried herbs is to use 1 teaspoon of dried for each 3 teaspoons of fresh. In the off season when using dried herbs it can help to mince about 1 teaspoon into a tablespoon of fresh curly parsley. This can simulate the freshness of some herbs.

Serves 8
Serving size = 1½ cups
Keeps well for about 48–72 hours in the refrigerator
Easily multiplied by 2

1 x 42oz tin tomato juice (no salt added)
2lb/900g fresh tomatoes (peeled and chopped)
1lb/450g cucumbers (peeled and diced)
¼ cup green peppers (diced)
¼ cup celery (diced)
¼ cup red onion (diced)
1½ tsp fresh tarragon
3 cloves garlic (finely chopped)

2 tsp Tabasco sauce
¼ cup red wine vinegar
½ tsp salt
1lb/450g fresh steamed shrimp (peeled & de-veined)
fresh ground black pepper

Combine all ingredients

Chill for at least 3 hours before serving

Add fresh ground black pepper to taste

"lycopenes have a beneficial effect on bad cholesterol"

" *A spoonful of honey will catch more flies than a gallon of vinegar*

Benjamin Franklin
Inventor, statesman
and philosopher

"

salads

Curried Chicken Salad

Calories 124

Calories from Fat 45

Total Fat 5g (8%)

Saturated Fat 1g (5%)

Cholesterol 17mg (6%)

Sodium 97mg (4%)

Total Carbohydrates 15g (5%)

Dietary Fibre 1g (4%)

Protein 7g

Vitamin A (5%)

Vitamin C (10%)

Calcium (4%)

Iron (3%)

Dr. Tim says...

Unfortunately, in this day and age you have to be very careful when handling chicken. The estimates of bacterial contamination are very high. A few simple rules can help keep you well:

- **Use the freshest chicken possible.**
- **If there is any odd odour don't use it.**
- **Rinse the chicken thoroughly in cold water prior to preparing it.**
- **Use a plastic cutting board when preparing.**
- **When finished, wash the board, your hands and knives in soapy water to reduce the risk of spreading the bacteria.**

Cooking chicken thoroughly is vital. Using a small instant thermometer check for the right temperatures. Poultry should reach 180°F/82°C in the thigh or 170°F/77°C in the breast.

Many free-range chickens are free of antibiotics and are fed carefully. However, there is no proof that this results in a bacteria-free bird, although most people agree that these chickens taste better.

Chef Tim says...

There are endless ways to make composed salads like chicken, shrimp or tuna salad. Don't be timid – the key to a healthier salad is using non-fat or low-fat wet ingredients like mayonnaise, sour cream or yogurt and use in smaller amounts, always measuring carefully.

Combining these with strong flavours like chutneys or salsas creates a rich taste using less fat and calories. A lot of chutneys don't have nutrition information on them. Assume that they have the same amount of calories as any jam.

Serves 6
Serving size = about ¾ cup
This recipe keeps well for about 36-48 hours in the refrigerator
Don't multiply

3 litres water
1 Tbl wine vinegar
½lb/225g chicken breasts
2 tsp curry powder
¼ cup low-fat mayonnaise
2 Tbl slivered almonds
¼ cup low-fat sour cream
¼ tsp cinnamon
2 Tbl your favourite chutney
¼ cup raisins
¼ cup spring onions (chopped)
½ cup celery (diced)
2 Tbl red pepper (diced)

Heat the water in a large frying pan until it begins to boil and then reduce the heat until the water is just below boiling. Add the vinegar, then the chicken breasts. Poach for about 15 minutes until the chicken is firm. Remove and chill.

Cut the chilled chicken into ½ inch cubes and place in a medium sized mixing bowl. Add all the other ingredients and fold together until well coated. Chill for at least an hour before serving.

There are endless ways to make composed salads "

9

Red Potato Salad

Calories	116
Calories from Fat	9
Total Fat 1g	(2%)
Saturated Fat 0g	(0%)
Cholesterol 2mg	(1%)
Sodium 126mg	(5%)
Total Carbohydrates 24g	(8%)
Dietary Fibre 2g	(8%)
Protein 3g	
Vitamin A	(2%)
Vitamin C	(25%)
Calcium	(1%)
Iron	(2%)

Dr. Tim says...

Take care. In medical school we learned to ask patients who had upset stomachs whether they had been to a picnic or a buffet meal recently. Unfortunately, most people who bring dishes to picnics or pot luck suppers (and many restaurants with buffets) don't think too much about how happy bacteria is to breed between 38ºF/8ºC and 160ºF/100ºC. They especially like room temperature. Do your friends a favour and take some ice packs to keep your delicious potato salad as cold as possible, or consider the next recipe...

the skins will generally just slip off

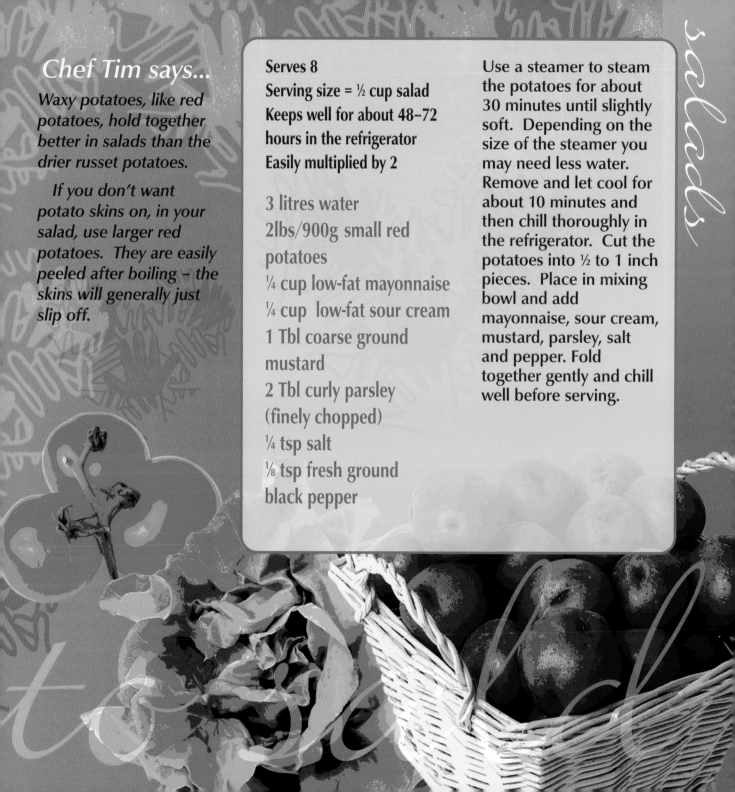

Chef Tim says...

Waxy potatoes, like red potatoes, hold together better in salads than the drier russet potatoes.

If you don't want potato skins on, in your salad, use larger red potatoes. They are easily peeled after boiling – the skins will generally just slip off.

Serves 8
Serving size = ½ cup salad
Keeps well for about 48–72 hours in the refrigerator
Easily multiplied by 2

3 litres water
2lbs/900g small red potatoes
¼ cup low-fat mayonnaise
¼ cup low-fat sour cream
1 Tbl coarse ground mustard
2 Tbl curly parsley (finely chopped)
¼ tsp salt
⅛ tsp fresh ground black pepper

Use a steamer to steam the potatoes for about 30 minutes until slightly soft. Depending on the size of the steamer you may need less water. Remove and let cool for about 10 minutes and then chill thoroughly in the refrigerator. Cut the potatoes into ½ to 1 inch pieces. Place in mixing bowl and add mayonnaise, sour cream, mustard, parsley, salt and pepper. Fold together gently and chill well before serving.

This recipe will work best with fresh herbs...

Vinaigrette Potato Salad

Calories	119
Calories from Fat	18
Total Fat	2g (3%)
Saturated Fat	0g (0%)
Cholesterol	0mg (0%)
Sodium	150mg (6%)
Total Carbohydrates	41g (14%)
Dietary Fibre	2g (8%)
Protein	2g
Vitamin A	(6%)
Vitamin C	(25%)
Calcium	(1%)
Iron	(7%)

Dr. Tim says...

Salt is salt. Many chefs and food writers will say that using one of the many gourmet salts on the market is better than the other stuff, but for the most part salt is salt.

Chef Tim says...

The thinly sliced red onions in this may be too strong for some people. Soaking onions in cold water for a long time before using them raw on a salad really works. Slice the onions to the desired thickness and separate into rings. Place the rings in a bowl of ice water and put them in the fridge for about half an hour. Drain the onions and pat dry.

This recipe will work best with fresh herbs sprinkled on it the last minute. If fresh dill is not available, try tarragon, basil or flat-leaf parsley.

Serves 8
Serving size = about ½ cup
This recipe keeps well for about 3 days in the refrigerator
Easily multiplied by 2

3 litres water
1½ lbs/700g small red potatoes
2 Tbl shallots (finely chopped)
2 Tbl red wine vinegar
1 Tbl extra virgin olive oil
¼ tsp salt
Fresh ground black pepper to taste
⅓ large red onion (sliced into very thin rings)
2 Tbl fresh dill

Steam the potatoes for about 30 minutes until slightly soft. Depending on the size of the steamer you may need less water. Rinse with cold water. Cut the potatoes into ½ to 1 inch pieces. Place in a large mixing bowl and add the shallots, vinegar, olive oil and salt.

Gently fold the salad until well blended. Add fresh ground pepper to taste while folding. Chill well before serving.

When ready to serve, place the sliced onions over the top of the salad and sprinkle with dill.

Some chefs claim that kosher salt tastes saltier. This is true only because the crystals are larger and less likely to dissolve completely on the food, so that the crystals that remain dissolve on the tongue more directly, activating the salt taste buds. There is a slight difference between the amount of sodium in a teaspoon of large salt crystals and regular table salt. Again, this is because the larger, irregular salt crystals take up more room in the spoon.

Sea salt is popular as well and there are chefs who swear by using special varieties. The sodium chloride that makes up sea salt is the same as that in granulated or kosher salt. It is the impurities in sea salts that account for differences in flavour.

Tomato Chive Dressing

Calories 49

Calories from Fat 23

Total Fat 2.5g (4%)

Saturated Fat <1g (<1%)

Cholesterol 0mg (0%)

Sodium 277mg (12%)

Total Carbohydrates 7g (2%)

Dietary Fibre 1g (4%)

Protein 1g

Vitamin A (11%)

Vitamin C (19%)

Calcium (23%)

Iron (4%)

Dr. Tim says...

Maple syrup is a great choice for all types of cooking. It helps distribute ingredients throughout your mouth, feeling much the same way fat does. Because of this 'mouthfeel' maple syrup, used carefully, can help reduce the amount of fat and calories in a recipe like this dressing, while enhancing other flavours. It also adds a rich, sweet, caramelized flavour to recipes.

1 Tbl maple syrup = 52 calories, <1g fat, 0g sat fat, 0g mono fat, 0g protein, 13g carbohydrates, 2mg sodium, 0mg cholesterol

Chef Tim says...

Try dressings made from ingredients that you have around the house. Adding fresh herbs like the chopped chives will give it a fresh summer flavour. Both the stem and the flower of the chive are edible and the purple flowers make for a lovely garnish.

Serves 6
Serving size = ¼ cup dressing
This dressing will keep well for about a week in the refrigerator
Easily multiplied by 2

1 5oz/150g can low-sodium V8 or tomato juice
1 Tbl extra virgin olive oil
2 Tbl tomato paste
2 Tbl coarse ground Dijon mustard
2 Tbl red wine vinegar
1 Tbl pure maple syrup

¼ tsp salt
2 Tbl chives (chopped)
2 cloves garlic (finely chopped)

Add all ingredients to a shaker bottle and shake vigorously. Chill for at least two hours before serving.

"the purple flowers make for a lovely garnish"

Thai Cucumber Salad

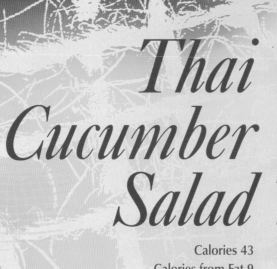

Calories	43
Calories from Fat	9
Total Fat	1g (2%)
Saturated Fat	<1g (0%)
Cholesterol	0mg (0%)
Sodium	3mg (<1%)
Total Carbohydrates	9g (3%)
Dietary Fibre	1g (5%)
Protein	1g
Vitamin A	(4%)
Vitamin C	(11%)
Calcium	(2%)
Iron	(4%)

A spoonful of honey will catch more flies than a gallon of vinegar.

Benjamin Franklin
inventor, statesman, and
philosopher

Dr. Tim says...

There is good evidence that eating legumes, like peanuts, lowers the risk of heart disease. Research, looking at almost 10,000 men, showed that even one serving of lentils or chick peas a week lowers the risk of heart disease. And the best part is that the more you eat, the lower the risk; with eating legumes 4 times or more per week reducing the risk of heart disease by as much as 22%. Peanuts have a great flavour whether raw or roasted and, if unsalted, they have almost no sodium.

Chef Tim says...

For frequent slicing, consider the benefits of a mandoline, if you don't already have one. At its most basic, a mandoline is a rectangular frame that holds an adjustable cutting blade in the centre of a sliding surface. Moving food back and forth over the blade creates uniform slices.

A small plastic version of this can be found in almost any kitchen store for less than a cheap bottle of wine. The blades are generally extremely sharp and don't discriminate between a carrot and the tips of fingers! Practise with cucumbers first before trying more solid foods like beets or carrots.

Serves 4
Serving size = about 1 cup salad
Leftovers keep for up to 24 hours in the refrigerator
Easily multiplied by 2 or 3

1 cup rice vinegar
1 tsp lime zest
¼ tsp Tabasco sauce
2 Tbl Splenda sugar substitute
½ cup red onion (diced)
2 large cucumbers (peeled and thinly sliced)
¼ cup fresh coriander leaves
1 Tbl raw peanuts (chopped)

Combine the rice vinegar, lime zest, Tabasco, Splenda, red onion, cucumber slices and coriander leaves in a non-reactive bowl. You can add the peanuts and let them marinate and they will be slightly chewy. Or, sprinkle them over the top of the salad just before serving. Marinate for at least 2 hours.

*1oz/28g peanuts=
161 calories, 14g fat,
2g sat fat, 7g mono fat,
1g protein,
5g carbohydrates,
5mg sodium,
0mg cholesterol.*

13

Caesar Salad

Calories 85

Calories from Fat 18

Total Fat 2g (3%)

Saturated Fat 1g (4%)

Cholesterol 6mg (2%)

Sodium 195mg (8%)

Total Carbohydrates 12g (4%)

Dietary Fibre 2g (8%)

Protein 6g

Vitamin A (43%)

Vitamin C (37%)

Calcium (16%)

Iron (7%)

Dr. Tim says...

Picking out key flavours can help to make a higher fat or higher calorie recipe into one that tastes the same but is great for you. With Caesar Salad dressing the key flavours are garlic, mustard, anchovies and Parmesan. Because Caesar dressing gets its creamy texture from oil and egg, I look for substitute ingredients that will give a similar, what I call, 'mouthfeel'. In this case, the combination of honey and yogurt makes for a rich texture. Dressings are an easy way to learn how to change recipes. In this recipe the non-fat yogurt, by itself, isn't quite as creamy as an egg and oil mixture. Honey works well because it adds sweetness (that both the oil and egg have) and contributes to a rich feel in the mouth.

2 tinned anchovy fillets = 17 calories, <1g fat, 0g sat fat, 0g mono fat, 2g protein, 0g carbohydrates, 293mg sodium, 7mg cholesterol.

the combination of honey and yogurt makes for a rich texture

Chef Tim says...

Most people would say they don't like anchovies but used carefully they can add a rich, savoury flavour to recipes and they are low in fat. It doesn't take much – usually 2–3 in a recipe. Each fillet has about 150mg of sodium so when adding anchovies decrease the amount of salt in the recipe.

Serves 8
Serving size = 1 small salad
The dressing keeps well tightly sealed in the refrigerator for about 5–7 days
Easily multiplied by 2

2 cloves garlic (finely chopped)
2 anchovy fillets
¼ tsp ground black pepper
2 Tbl fresh lemon juice
1½ oz/40g Parmigiano-Reggiano Parmesan cheese (grated)
½ cup non-fat yogurt
2 Tbl Dijon mustard
2 Tbl honey
2 heads romaine lettuce
1 cup low-fat croutons

Place the garlic, anchovies, pepper, lemon juice, mustard, honey, Parmesan cheese and yogurt in a blender and process until smooth. Chill for at least 2 hours.

  Rinse the lettuce, drain and spin dry. Cut crosswise and place in refrigerator until needed. Toss the dressing together with the romaine lettuce and croutons.

My doctor told me to stop having intimate dinners for four. Unless there are three other people

Orson Welles
Filmmaker

14

Eggs Benedict

Calories 187
Calories from Fat 63
Total Fat 7g (12%)
Saturated Fat 2g (10%)
Cholesterol 242mg (94%)
Sodium 281mg (12%)
Total Carbohydrates 20g (7%)
Dietary Fibre 2g (8%)
Protein 11g
Vitamin A (17%)
Vitamin C (20%)
Calcium (8%)
Iron (12%)

Dr. Tim says...

Traditional Eggs Benedict calls for bacon instead of asparagus. Substituting a 2oz slice of lean ham for the asparagus adds 104 calories, 5g of fat and 2g of saturated fat. The sodium tips the scales at 875mg, very high for a salt restricted diet. The asparagus is only 13 calories, so good for you, and it's so elegant!

so good for you, and it's so elegant!

savouries

Chef Tim says...

Acidulated water is water to which a small amount of an acid is added (such as vinegar, lemon juice or lime juice) to prevent discoloration of some fruits and vegetables (such as apples, pears and artichokes) that brown when their cut surfaces are exposed to air.

The lower pH of acidulated water helps proteins (such as those in eggs or fish) to cook properly.

Serves 1
Serving size = 1 egg/½ English muffin/2 Tbl Sauce
Eat immediately
Easily multiplied

Hollandaise Sauce, the next recipe in the book, needs to be made first and be hot.

2 litres water
1 Tbl white wine vinegar
5 asparagus spears (blanched)
½ English muffin
1 large egg
2 Tbl Hollandaise sauce (see next recipe)

Divide the water between two pans. In one add the vinegar to make 'acidulated water' for poaching the eggs.

Ensure that the water never boils in either pan, but remains at the 'shiver' stage, perfect for both poaching and blanching. Reheat the asparagus in the plain water for 2–3 minutes.

Crack the egg into a cup or onto a plate and slide gently into the acidulated water. Now toast the half English muffin. By the time the muffin is ready the asparagus and egg should be nearly done. The Hollandaise has to be hot, but not so hot that the egg in the sauce will overcook and curdle. Serve the blanched asparagus spears on the toasted half muffin, followed by the poached egg. Top with 2 Tbl of Hollandaise sauce.

Hollandaise Sauce

Calories 29

Calories from Fat 13

Total Fat 1.5g (2%)

Saturated Fat <1g (<1%)

Cholesterol 30mg (10%)

Sodium 85mg (4%)

Total Carbohydrates 3g (1%)

Dietary Fibre 0g (0%)

Protein 1g

Vitamin A (2%)

Vitamin C (4%)

Calcium (2%)

Iron (0%)

Dr. Tim says...

Look for the flavours and textures in traditional recipes that maximize taste without sacrifice. Great tasting and healthy recipes depend on two aspects of food, what I call the "key flavours" and "mouthfeel".

maximize taste without sacrifice

Chef Tim says...

Cornflour is the finely milled endosperm of corn kernels and is an excellent thickening agent that results in clear sauces with a silky sheen. Here are a few pointers for using cornflour:

1. It has twice the thickening power of wheat flour and it produces a clearer sauce.

2. If thickening acidic liquids such as juices, vinegars, wines, the thickening power will be halved.

3. It is best to mix with an equal amount of cold liquid before incorporating it into a sauce as it clumps easily.

4. If the sauce is overheated or over stirred it will begin to break down and lose thickening power.

Serves 8 for Eggs Benedict (or any other yummy recipe)
Serving size = 2 Tbl
Use immediately
Do not multiply

1½ Tbl cornflour
⅔ cup semi-skimmed milk
1 tsp unsalted butter
2½ Tbl fresh lemon juice
1 egg yolk
½ tsp salt

In a small stainless or enamelled pan cook cornflour and milk on medium heat. Whisk continuously until sauce begins to thicken. Reduce heat to low and add the butter, whisking until melted. Slowly add the lemon juice and the salt and whisk until well blended. Whisk in the egg yolk until smooth. Serve as soon as possible.

16

Courgette and Chèvre Frittata

Calories 248

Calories from Fat 117

Total Fat 13g (20%)

Saturated Fat 7g (28%)

Cholesterol 237mg (79%)

Sodium 425mg (18%)

Carbohydrates 14g (5%)

Dietary Fibre 3g (12%)

Protein 18g

Vitamin A (15%)

Vitamin C (25%)

Calcium (20%)

Iron (9%)

Dr. Tim says...

Using a little bit of a rich cheese makes for a really tasty dish and avoids the fat and calories caused by using more of a lower fat cheese. Remember, weigh those ingredients!

You can sometimes lower the fat and cholesterol in egg dishes by using fewer egg yolks. In some cases this is easy and changes the finished dish only slightly (Frittata, Tortilla, Omelette).

Care must be taken with other recipes, especially with baking where the fat in egg yolks works especially well. Simply changing the ratio of egg yolk or egg whites, without a correction in other ingredients, can give disappointing results.

"...makes for a really tasty dish and avoids the fa

Chef Tim says...

If you want to lower the fat but keep some of the flavour, the oil spray can is a good addition to the kitchen. Choose a can that will spray oil after being pumped. These are reasonably priced at kitchen shops and will take any type of oil.

nd calories...

Serves 2
Serving size = ½ pie
Will keep 5 days if refrigerated and wrapped well
Leftovers are excellent for sandwiches
Easily multiplied by 2 but requires a larger pan

1 medium courgette (sliced thin lengthwise)
Olive oil spray
1 tsp unsalted butter
1 clove garlic (finely chopped)
½ red onion (sliced)
2 large eggs
2 large egg whites
2 Tbl water
⅛ tsp salt
2 Tbl Parmigiano-Reggiano Parmesan cheese (grated)
1oz/28g semi-soft goat cheese
fresh ground black pepper

Preheat the oven to 425°F/220°C.
Lay the courgette slices on a baking tray and spray lightly with the olive oil. Roast for about 7–10 minutes, turning once. Remove and cool.

In a non-stick frying pan on low-medium heat, melt ½ tsp butter and add the garlic. Do not allow the garlic to brown. Add the sliced red onion and cook until translucent. Set aside. Whisk the eggs, egg whites, water and salt in a bowl until frothy. Fold in the Parmigiano-Reggiano.

Heat the remaining butter in a small non-stick frying pan over high heat and when bubbling add the egg mixture. Reduce to medium heat and simmer for about 2 minutes.

Add the onion/garlic mixture, distributing it across the top of the eggs. Layer the courgette slices on top in a crisscross pattern and then crumble the goat's cheese over the top of the courgette. Grind fresh pepper on top to taste. Bake for about 15 minutes in the oven until it puffs and is firm to the touch.

17

"This dish is great right out of the oven"

Tortilla

Calories 173
Calories from Fat 45
Total Fat 5g (8%)
Saturated Fat 1g (5%)
Cholesterol 106mg (35%)
Sodium 264mg (11%)
Total Carbohydrates 21g (7%)
Dietary Fibre 2g (8%)
Protein 11g
Vitamin A (4%)
Vitamin C (25%)
Calcium (3%)
Iron (4%)

Dr. Tim says...

In an epidemiological study conducted in Spain, 171 heart attack patients were compared with people who had no evidence of coronary disease. Those who ate the most olive oil, an average of about 4 Tbl per day, had the lowest risk for heart attack. The group eating only about ½ Tbl per day had the highest risk of heart attack. The researchers feel there is a causal association between the olive oil and reduction of coronary disease, but feel that a larger study is needed to definitively prove this.

Chef Tim says...

This dish is great right out of the oven but is even better the next day after it has chilled. This is the most common way that it is served in Spain and can be found all over the country in Tapas bars. Because the tortilla is made with eggs be careful to keep it well chilled before serving.

Serves 4, hot or cold
Serving size = ¼ pie
Will keep well for about
24–48 hours
Can be multiplied by 2 if using
a larger pan

3 litres water
¾ lb/340g red or
Yukon gold potatoes
8 large egg whites
2 large egg yolks
1 Tbl fresh curly parsley
(finely chopped)
¼ tsp salt
2 tsp fresh oregano (finely
chopped)
⅛ tsp red pepper flakes
½ tsp jalapeño (finely
chopped)
fresh ground black pepper
to taste
2 tsp extra virgin olive oil
1 medium white onion
(chopped)

Place the water in a medium stockpot over high heat and bring to a boil. Reduce the heat to medium-high and cook the potatoes until slightly tender (about 20 minutes). Drain and let the potatoes cool slightly. Cut into ½ inch cubes. Preheat the oven to 350°F/175°C. Whisk together the egg whites, egg yolks, parsley, salt, oregano, red pepper flakes and finely chopped jalapeño. Add fresh ground pepper to taste and then add the potatoes. Fold together gently until well blended. Heat the olive oil in a 10 inch non-stick skillet over high heat and add the onions. Cook, stirring continuously, until soft and golden brown. Reduce the heat to medium and add the eggs/potato mixture. Cook for 2 minutes on the stove and then transfer to the oven and cook for about 20 minutes (until the centre is set).

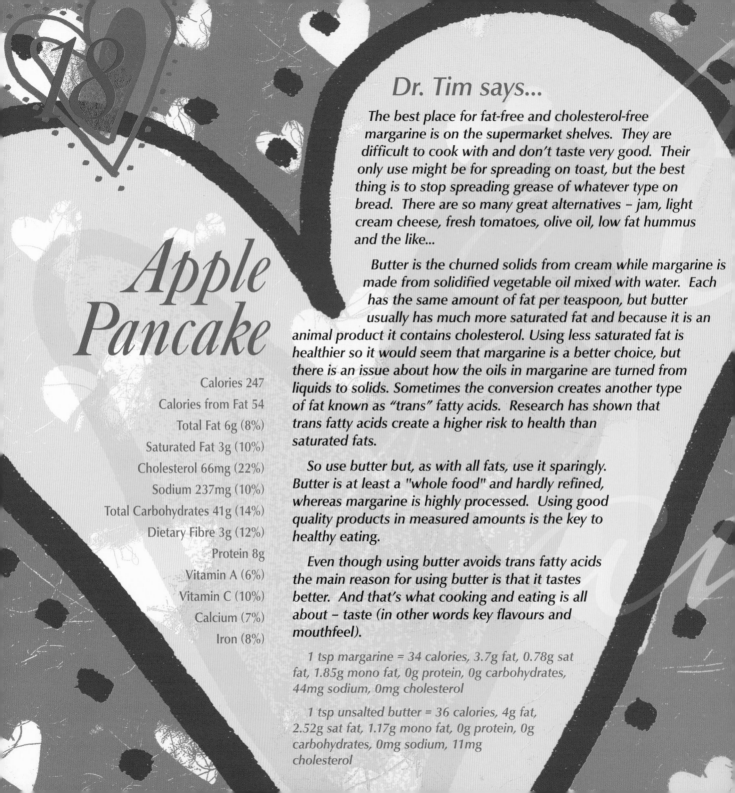

18

Apple Pancake

Calories 247

Calories from Fat 54

Total Fat 6g (8%)

Saturated Fat 3g (10%)

Cholesterol 66mg (22%)

Sodium 237mg (10%)

Total Carbohydrates 41g (14%)

Dietary Fibre 3g (12%)

Protein 8g

Vitamin A (6%)

Vitamin C (10%)

Calcium (7%)

Iron (8%)

Dr. Tim says...

The best place for fat-free and cholesterol-free margarine is on the supermarket shelves. They are difficult to cook with and don't taste very good. Their only use might be for spreading on toast, but the best thing is to stop spreading grease of whatever type on bread. There are so many great alternatives – jam, light cream cheese, fresh tomatoes, olive oil, low fat hummus and the like...

Butter is the churned solids from cream while margarine is made from solidified vegetable oil mixed with water. Each has the same amount of fat per teaspoon, but butter usually has much more saturated fat and because it is an animal product it contains cholesterol. Using less saturated fat is healthier so it would seem that margarine is a better choice, but there is an issue about how the oils in margarine are turned from liquids to solids. Sometimes the conversion creates another type of fat known as "trans" fatty acids. Research has shown that trans fatty acids create a higher risk to health than saturated fats.

So use butter but, as with all fats, use it sparingly. Butter is at least a "whole food" and hardly refined, whereas margarine is highly processed. Using good quality products in measured amounts is the key to healthy eating.

Even though using butter avoids trans fatty acids the main reason for using butter is that it tastes better. And that's what cooking and eating is all about – taste (in other words key flavours and mouthfeel).

1 tsp margarine = 34 calories, 3.7g fat, 0.78g sat fat, 1.85g mono fat, 0g protein, 0g carbohydrates, 44mg sodium, 0mg cholesterol

1 tsp unsalted butter = 36 calories, 4g fat, 2.52g sat fat, 1.17g mono fat, 0g protein, 0g carbohydrates, 0mg sodium, 11mg cholesterol

Chef Tim says...

I put this recipe in the Savouries section because I like it so much and I didn't have any other place to put it. It is the perfect dish for a special occasion brunch.

Substituting Splenda cuts the calories but not the sweetness (one of the key flavours). When granulated sugar is melted it is clear, but as it heats further the liquid turns to a clear light brown syrup. The longer the syrup is heated the darker the colour. Fruits, like apples, and vegetables like onions, that contain natural sugars can be heated so that their natural sugars change in the same way.

This is commonly referred to as caramelizing and results in a concentrated, sweet flavour with a golden syrupy glaze without needing to add refined sugar.

Serves 4
Serving size = ¼ pancake
Leftovers are actually pretty good
Wrap tightly after cooled and refrigerate
To multiply by 2, make 2 separate batches in 2 pans

2 lbs/900g (4 medium) Granny Smith apples
2 tsp unsalted butter
½ cup Splenda sugar substitute
¼ cup water
3 large egg whites
1 large egg yolk
¾ cup non-fat buttermilk
¾ cup all-purpose flour
¼ tsp salt
2 Tbl Splenda sugar substitute
2 tsp unsalted butter

Peel, core and thinly slice the apples. Preheat oven to 425°F/220°C.

In a 12 inch thick-based non-stick frying pan heat the butter, Splenda and water until boiling. Add apples and cook about 15 minutes. Stir gently about every 3 minutes. As the apples cook the liquid will reduce and the mixture will turn a light golden brown caramel colour. The bottom of the apples should be a caramel brown.

As the apples cook blend the egg whites, egg yolk, buttermilk, flour, salt and the 2 Tbl Splenda until smooth. Pour over the caramelized apples so that the liquid covers them completely. Transfer the pan to the oven and bake for about 15–18 minutes.

The pancake is done when it is puffed and brown on top. Remove from the oven and dot immediately with 2 tsp butter.

it is the perfect dish for a special occasion brunch

19

Fettuccine Alfredo

Calories 332

Calories from Fat 99

Total Fat 11g (17%)

Saturated Fat 6g (30%)

Cholesterol 28mg (9%)

Sodium 367mg (15%)

Total Carbohydrates 37g (12%)

Dietary Fibre 2g (5%)

Protein 18g

Vitamin A (6%)

Vitamin C (2%)

Calcium (23%)

Iron (13%)

Dr. Tim says...

This recipe is a good example of how to use "key flavours" and "mouthfeel" to develop recipes. The key flavours are Parmesan, garlic and olive oil. Emphasizing these ingredients to enhance them while looking for ways to reduce fat and calories is the secret to healthier recipes without compromising flavour.

The easiest way to reduce the amount of the rich ingredients, like Parmesan or olive oil, is to always cook with the best quality products.

Because Parmigiano-Reggiano has so much more flavour than the anonymous ready grated Parmesan, less is needed. The same holds true for using a high quality, fruity, extra virgin olive oil. Pay attention to every ingredient. Even though the garlic doesn't have many calories, buying the freshest garlic and storing it carefully makes for the most flavourful dish. The creamy texture that usually comes from an excess of cheap, lesser quality cheese and oil, is created by using lower fat cheese like the semi-soft goat's cheese and semi-skimmed milk. The result is the same intense flavour and creamy feel with less fat and calories.

Chef Tim says...

Eating healthily is as much about the amount of food eaten as anything else.

Throughout this book the serving sizes of different foods are highlighted.

A serving size of pasta is 2oz with each serving having about 200 calories. There is usually not much fat in pasta, about a gram or so per serving. Most pasta is simply flour and water.

Serves 2
Serving size = 2oz pasta with sauce
Leftovers are fair at best
Easily multiplied by 2, 3 or 4

1 tsp extra virgin olive oil
2 cloves garlic (finely chopped)
2 tsp all-purpose flour
⅓ cup semi-skimmed milk (chilled)
1oz/28g soft goat cheese
1oz/28g Parmigiano-Reggiano Parmesan cheese (grated)
4 litres water
¼ lb/113g fettuccine
2 Tbl fresh curly parsley (finely chopped)

In a non-stick frying pan over medium heat, cook the olive oil and garlic very slowly, stirring frequently. Do not allow the garlic to brown or it will become bitter. Reduce heat to low and slowly add the flour. Stir continuously to blend the oil and flour. Cook gently for about 1 minute and do not allow the mixture to turn brown. Slowly add the milk, whisking to keep the sauce from forming clumps. When the sauce is smooth and begins to thicken, add the goat's cheese and whisk as it melts. When the sauce is smooth add the Parmigiano-Reggiano and whisk as it melts until the sauce is creamy. Reduce the heat to very low. Heat the water to a boil, in a large pan. Add the fettuccine and cook until just tender (about 12–15 minutes for dried pasta). Drain well and then add the pasta to the sauce, tossing to coat thoroughly. Sprinkle the parsley over the top and serve.

20

Basil Pesto

Calories 88
Calories from Fat 72
Total Fat 8g (12%)
Saturated Fat 2g (10%)
Cholesterol 4mg (1%)
Sodium 89mg (4%)
Total Carbohydrates 5g (<1%)
Dietary Fibre <1g (<1%)
Protein 4g
Vitamin A (22%)
Vitamin C (10%)
Calcium (11%)
Iron (7%)

Dr. Tim says...

Pesto is essentially made of fats (Parmesan, olive oil and pine nuts) that are held together by basil (or sometimes other greens like dill). This recipe works to maximise the flavour and reduce the calories, but there's still a fair amount of both fat and calories. Measuring sauces like pesto is crucial. Use a tablespoon to measure the amount that a recipe calls for. Not only will the dish taste correct but there's no guesswork in the serving sizes.

Chef Tim says...

Using a little lemon juice helps to keep pesto from turning brown. It's actually the ascorbic acid (also known as Vitamin C) in the lemon juice that keeps the basil from oxidising. This same trick can be used for other recipes where a fruit or vegetable might turn brown. Try using lime juice in guacamole – the flavour of limes and avocado together is perfect and the avocado will remain bright green.

Serves 6
Serving size = 2 Tbl
Freezes fairly well
Keeps sealed in the refrigerator 3–4 days
Easily multiplied by 2, 3 or 4

2 Tbl pine nuts
2 cloves garlic (finely chopped)
4 cups fresh basil leaves (there is no substitute for fresh basil in this recipe: dried basil has a completely different flavour)
1oz Parmigiano-Reggiano Parmesan cheese (grated)
2 Tbl water
1 Tbl fresh lemon juice
1 Tbl white wine vinegar
2 Tbl extra virgin olive oil

Blend all the ingredients until smooth.

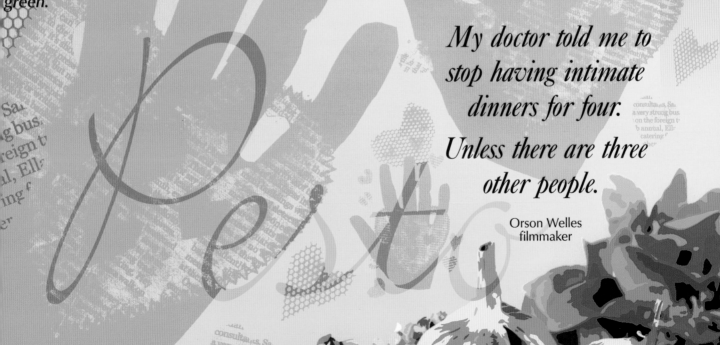

My doctor told me to stop having intimate dinners for four.

Unless there are three other people.

Orson Welles
filmmaker

21

Barbecue Chicken

For ¼ cup Barbecue Sauce

Calories 80

Calories from Fat 0

Total Fat 0g (12%)

Saturated Fat 0g (10%)

Cholesterol 0mg (31%)

Sodium 33mg (1%)

Total Carbohydrates 20g (7%)

Dietary Fibre <1g (2%)

Protein 0g

Vitamin A (6%)

Vitamin C (9%)

Calcium (1%)

Iron (3%)

Dr. Tim says...

One sodium molecule and one chloride molecule are joined in the crystal we call salt. In the body they break down into sodium and chloride. The amount of sodium is what is important in a healthy diet. The recommendation is that you have about 2400mg of sodium. Because one teaspoon of salt is 2325mg of sodium it's pretty easy to keep track – a healthy diet is about a teaspoon a day. Low-sodium ingredients put you in control of the amount of sodium in your recipes.

Nutrients (¼ lb/113g portion)	Skinless chicken thigh	Skinless chicken breast	Skinless chicken leg
Calories	135	125	136
Fat g	4.4	1.4	4.3
Sodium mg	97	74	98
Saturated Fat g	1.1	0.4	1.1
Cholesterol mg	94	66	94
Protein g	1.4	0.3	22

Chef Tim says...

This barbecue sauce is so easy to make and has no fat and almost no sodium. You can use it almost anywhere – on grilled chicken or even fish like tuna, salmon or shrimp. Just use the table opposite to determine the amount of calories, fat and sodium of your favourite piece of chicken.

Serves 8
Serving size = ¼ lb/113g
chicken with ¼ cup sauce
Leftovers are great
refrigerated for no more
than 2 days
Easily multiplied by 2, 3 or 4

1 cup low-sodium ketchup
¼ cup apricot jam
¼ cup firmly packed dark brown sugar
½ cup cider vinegar
1 Tbl Worcestershire sauce
2 tsp water
⅛ tsp hot sauce

⅛ tsp garlic powder
½ tsp dry mustard
1 tsp chilli powder
1 tsp paprika
1 tsp ground black pepper
8 pieces skinless chicken
(breast, thigh, drumstick)

Blend all ingredients except the chicken and chill overnight. Heat grill to medium heat (approx. 350°F/175°C). Dip chicken pieces in the barbecue sauce and place on the grill. Turn frequently, spreading the rest of the sauce on the chicken as it cooks.

"you can use it almost anywhere"

22

French Fries

Calories 105

Calories from Fat 18

Total Fat 2g (3%)

Saturated Fat <1g (<1%)

Cholesterol 0mg (0%)

Sodium 79mg (3%)

Total Carbohydrates 20g (7%)

Dietary Fibre 2g (8%)

Protein 2g

Vitamin A (0%)

Vitamin C (37%)

Calcium (<1%)

Iron (5%)

Dr. Tim says...

Many recipes for French Fries (as well as other potato recipes) recommend soaking in cold water for 30 minutes. The rationale is that some of the starch is leached away. The starch on the outside edges of the cut potatoes may wash away, but significant starch or nutrients are not likely to be changed. What is more likely is that the inside of a chilled potato takes longer to cook. Consequently the outside will be crispy and the inside soft and moist.

This recipe was tested both ways, with and without soaking the cut potatoes, and the soaked potatoes were lighter and fluffier on the inside and crispy on the outside.

... lighter and fluffier on th

Chef Tim says...

Oven fried foods taste just like deep fried ones, if you handle them right. Most of the time you have to eat the dish right away.

These French Fries, for instance, will keep for all of about 20 minutes (about the same amount of time as ones that have been deep fried).

Serves 4
Serving size = ¼lb/113g fries
Eat immediately
Easily multiplied by 2 but must be cooked in 2 batches

1lb/450g roasting potatoes (peeled and cut into ¼ inch strips)
1 litre chilled water
1 tray ice cubes
⅛ tsp salt
spray rape-seed oil

After the potatoes are peeled and sliced, place them in a mixing bowl with cold water and ice cubes. Soak for 30 minutes.

Preheat oven to 400°F/205°C. Drain potatoes and pat dry.

Put potatoes and salt in a plastic bag or lidded box and spray with rape-seed oil for about 3 seconds. Shake, to coat the potatoes well with the oil and salt.

Lay the potatoes on a baking tray, ensuring they do not touch each other, and spray lightly with the rape-seed oil. Bake for about 7 minutes, turn, bake for a further 7 minutes and turn again. Total cooking time will be 20–25 minutes. Serve immediately.

...side and crispy on the outside.

23 Oven Fried Chicken

Melba toast is an amazing bread coating!

Calories 284
Calories from Fat 36
Total Fat 4g (6%)
Saturated Fat 1g (5%)
Cholesterol 119mg (39%)
Sodium 581mg (24%)
Total Carbohydrates 27g (9%)
Dietary Fibre 2g (9%)
Protein 33g
Vitamin A (2%)
Vitamin C (3%)
Calcium (6%)
Iron (13%)

Dr. Tim says...

Fried chicken doesn't have to be fried to taste like fried chicken. Melba toast is an amazing bread coating!

3 pieces Melba toast = 50 calories, 0g fat, 0g sat fat, 0g mono fat, 2g protein, 11g carbohydrates, 90mg sodium, 0mg cholesterol.

Chef Tim says...

When coating ingredients with bread crumbs use one hand for the liquid coating and the other hand for the crumbs. Doing it this way keeps your hands from getting all gummed up with bread crumbs.

Serves 4
Serving size = ¼ lb/113g chicken
Keeps well for 2 days
Easily multiplied by 2, 3 or 4

1 large egg
1 large egg white
1 Tbl Dijon mustard
5oz/140g plain Melba toast
1 tsp dried thyme
1 tsp dried rosemary
½ tsp dried oregano
¼ tsp garlic powder
¼ tsp salt
¼ tsp ground black pepper
¼ tsp cayenne pepper
4 ¼ lb/113g boneless, skinless chicken breasts
spray oil

In a small bowl whisk the egg, egg white and Dijon mustard until smooth. In a food processor crumb the Melba toast, thyme, rosemary, oregano, garlic powder, salt, black pepper and cayenne pepper. Leave some pieces about the size of currants. Preheat oven to 400°F/205°C. First dredge a chicken breast in the egg mixture, coating it thoroughly and then dredge in the bread crumbs, patting and turning frequently until well coated. Place the chicken on a baking sheet and bake for 3 minutes, then lightly spray the top of each chicken breast with oil. Bake 5 minutes more and then turn. Spray lightly with the oil again and bake for about 6 more minutes. This recipe works well with any piece of chicken (with or without the bone). Use skinless legs, thighs or breasts.

Cornbread Muffins

Calories 109

Calories from Fat 18

Total Fat 2g (3%)

Saturated Fat 1g (5%)

Cholesterol 22mg (7%)

Sodium 248mg (10%)

Total Carbohydrates 20g (7%)

Dietary Fibre 1g (4%)

Protein 3g

Vitamin A (2%)

Vitamin C (<1%)

Calcium (10%)

Iron (5%)

Dr. Tim says...

Size does matter. For the most part eggs come in 3 different sizes: medium, large and extra large. The recipes in this book are written using large eggs. The nutrition information is based on large eggs. Using an extra large egg will increase the nutrients by about 20%, including calories, fat and cholesterol, so take care when choosing egg size.

Chef Tim says...

As with all baked goods, this recipe contains fat. Measuring the egg and butter correctly provides enough to give the cornbread body and a rich taste.

With baking or making desserts, measuring is important because baking is basically chemistry and success depends on exact use of ingredients.

Serves 12
Serving size = 1 muffin
Keeps well for about 3 days if sealed
Do not multiply – make separate batches

¾ cup yellow cornmeal
1 cup all-purpose flour
⅓ cup sugar
1 Tbl baking powder
½ tsp salt
1 cup non-fat buttermilk
1 large egg
1 Tbl unsalted butter (melted)

Mix all ingredients together in a bowl. Let stand for 5 to 10 minutes. Line a non-stick muffin tin with muffin papers. Divide the batter into 12 muffins and bake at 325°F/165°C for about 15 minutes until golden on top.

Here's a rule of thumb for substitution: 5 large eggs = 4 extra large eggs = 6 medium eggs.

1 large egg = 75 calories, 5g fat, 1.5g sat fat, 2g mono fat, 6g protein, 0g carbohydrates, 63mg sodium, 212mg cholesterol

25

Roasted Garlic Mashed Potatoes

Calories 125
Calories from Fat 27
Total Fat 3g (5%)
Saturated Fat 2g (10%)
Cholesterol 8mg (3%)
Sodium 195mg (8%)
Total Carbohydrates 24g (8%)
Dietary Fibre 0g (0%)
Protein 3g
Vitamin A (2%)
Vitamin C (16%)
Calcium (13%)
Iron (40%)

Dr. Tim says...

The key to healthy mashed potatoes that are rich and creamy is the buttermilk/milk combination. The buttermilk adds richness and tartness with no fat, and the milk adds creaminess. The butter is used here only as a flavour enhancer.

½ cup non-fat buttermilk = 49 calories, 0g fat, 0g salt, 0g mono fat, 4g protein, 6g carbohydrates, 128mg sodium, 5mg cholesterol

"The buttermilk adds richness and tartness with no fat"

Chef Tim says...

Originally buttermilk was the sour liquid left after churning butter from milk. It is now made by adding a culture to skimmed milk to create a fermented product that is rich and creamy with a tart flavour. It can be used in soups and sauces instead of milk but must be heated gently or it will curdle. It may be salty so check the packaging.

Used in salad dressings, it adds the same tartness as sour cream but without the fat. When a recipe calls for mayonnaise and sour cream, substitute low-fat mayonnaise and buttermilk, or yogurt and buttermilk.

In baking, it acts very much like full-fat milk in recipes like pancakes and muffins and is ideal because there is no fat. Because of its higher acid content, the amount of baking powder or baking soda may need adjusting.

Buttermilk can easily be made by mixing 1 cup of skimmed milk with 1 tablespoon of any acid such as lemon juice or white wine vinegar. Alternatively, add a tablespoon of Cream of Tartar for a less acidic result.

Serves 4
Serving size = about 1 cup
Keeps fairly well for about 48 hours in the fridge
Easily multiplied by 2 or 3

For this recipe Roasted Garlic is needed, the next recipe in the book.
3 litres water
1lb/454g Yukon gold or red potatoes
2 tsp unsalted butter
⅓ cup non-fat buttermilk
⅓ cup 2% milk
¼ tsp salt
4 cloves roasted garlic (see next recipe)
Ground black pepper

Quarter the potatoes and put into a large pan, cover with about an inch of water. Bring to the boil and then reduce heat until the water is simmering. After about 15–20 minutes check if the potatoes are slightly soft in the middle. They should give when squeezed. Remove from heat and drain water. Add butter, buttermilk, milk, salt and roasted garlic. Mash potatoes until creamy and the roasted garlic is well blended in, yet leaving a few chunks. Take care not to over mash, as this will result in pasty potatoes. Add ground black pepper to taste.

26

Roasted Garlic

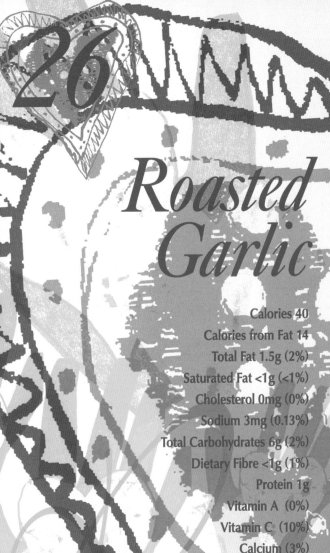

Calories 40

Calories from Fat 14

Total Fat 1.5g (2%)

Saturated Fat <1g (<1%)

Cholesterol 0mg (0%)

Sodium 3mg (0.13%)

Total Carbohydrates 6g (2%)

Dietary Fibre <1g (1%)

Protein 1g

Vitamin A (0%)

Vitamin C (10%)

Calcium (3%)

Iron (2%)

Dr. Tim says...

It has long been thought that garlic helps lower cholesterol, but it's not as effective as some research has indicated. Most of the studies were too small or not well enough designed to draw conclusions. In an analysis that looked at all of the smaller studies combined, it appears that there is a reduction in cholesterol when compared to placebo. This is, at best, a modest lowering of cholesterol – in the order of 5%, not the 10–20% as was once thought. This analysis did, however, only take into account the use of garlic pills and not fresh garlic.

Part of the problem in studying garlic is that researchers can't agree on what form of garlic to use. Also, it's important in research that test subjects are 'blinded' as to whether they are getting medication or placebo. This is difficult to do with garlic. Many preparations have a garlic smell or taste, making it difficult to keep the identity of the medication secret.

Clearly, garlic is not bad for you. It tastes great, is a fundamental ingredient in every kitchen, is low in calories (13 for 3 cloves), has essentially no fat or salt, no cholesterol, is pretty high in vitamin C and lowers cholesterol at least a little bit.

The only conclusion can be to eat more garlic.

Chef Tim says...

A garlic roaster is a great utensil. The best ones are made of clay and have a glazed dish so that the oil won't absorb into the clay. They're cheap and come in single bulb sizes but it's worth getting a bigger one that will roast four or five heads at a time.

Alternatively, using a pan that has a thick bottom will work fine. Reduce the heat in the oven by about 25°F/5°C depending on the thickness of the pan.

Serves 6
Serving size = ⅓ head of garlic (about 6 cloves)
Keeps well, tightly covered, for about 4–6 days
Easily multiplied

2 heads or corns
whole garlic
2 tsp extra virgin
olive oil

Preheat oven to 300°F/150°C. Peel the outermost skin of the head of garlic only, not the cloves.

With the bulb whole, turn on its side and slice ½ inch off the stem end. Pour the olive oil in the bottom of a heavy-bottom sauce pan. Place the garlic cut side down in the pan on top of the olive oil. Cover and roast for 45 minutes until cloves are slightly brown at the cut end and soft throughout.

"The only conclusion can b to eat more garlic."

27

Lemon Butter Brussels Sprouts

Calories 84

Calories from Fat 18

Total Fat 2g (3%)

Saturated Fat 1g (5%)

Cholesterol 5mg (1%)

Sodium 101mg (4%)

Total Carbohydrates 15g (5%)

Dietary Fibre 5g (16%)

Protein 4g

Vitamin A (22%)

Vitamin C (163%)

Calcium (5%)

Iron (9%)

Dr. Tim says...

For a long time people have thought that eating local honey would help with allergies. Unfortunately, it doesn't appear that this is the case. There is a beautifully designed study performed by Dr. T.V. Rajan at the University of Connecticut, where participants ate either local non-filtered honey, pasteurized honey, or corn syrup with honey flavour. Ten different allergy symptoms were measured. There were no differences between the people who ate the honey and the people eating the placebo honey.

Chef Tim says...

Brussels sprouts, like all vegetables, are best purchased fresh and used quickly. Buy small ones and try to use them immediately so there is less time for them to develop a bitter flavour. If a lot of vegetables are steaming, the ones at the bottom of the steamer cook faster than those on top. Stirring them works but is a hassle. Blanching beans, brussels sprouts, or asparagus, where the food is immersed briefly in water heated to 185°F/85°C gives more control over the process.

¼lb/113g brussels sprouts = 49 calories, 0g fat, 0g sat fat, 0g mono fat, 4g protein, 10g carbohydrates, 28mg sodium, 0mg cholesterol

There's also a lot of fibre in these little guys. Each serving has almost 5g.

Serves 4
Serving size = ¼lb/113g brussels sprouts
Not for keeping
Easily multiplied by 2 or 3

1lb/450g brussels sprouts (about 1 inch/2cm wide)
1 Tbl lemon juice
1 Tbl honey
⅛ tsp salt
2 tsp unsalted butter
2 cups water

Trim the stems from the sprouts and slice in half lengthwise. Place the water in a pan with a steamer basket and heat on high. Steam until slightly tender (about 10–15 minutes).

Meanwhile put the lemon juice, honey, salt and butter in a medium sized mixing bowl. Add the cooked sprouts to the bowl and toss until the butter is melted and the sauce well blended.

28

London Broil with Mushrooms Saut éed in Cognac

Calories 270

Calories from Fat 90

Total Fat 10g (15%)

Saturated Fat 3g (15%)

Cholesterol 70mg (35%)

Sodium 164mg (7%)

Total Carbohydrates 14g (5%)

Dietary Fibre 0g (0%)

Protein 44g

Vitamin A (68%)

Vitamin C (10%)

Calcium (2%)

Iron (23%)

Dr. Tim says...

Marbling is the fat that runs through the flesh of meat. When the meat is cooked, the fat melts and this helps keep the meat moist as well as giving flavour. It is a fallacy that more marbling makes for a more tender cut of beef.

For the most part, the marbling simply adds more fat. Where the meat comes from on the animal and how much the muscle has been used, the type of animal, how it is raised, what it is fed and how the meat is cooked, are far more important factors. Beef fillet, for instance, has very little marbled fat and is the most tender cut.

Chef Tim says...

When cooking meats it is important to remove them from the oven a little early. Flank steak should be allowed to "rest" for 5–10 minutes, but a larger cut needs to rest for at least 15 minutes.

After removing meat from the oven or grill the internal temperature of the meat continues to rise (some people call this carryover cooking). Without the continued high temperature of the oven the external temperature of the meat decreases, however, and the result is redistribution of the juices in the meat, making it both easier to carve as well as more succulent.

Serves 6
Serving size = ¼ lb/113g steak with about ½ cup mushrooms
Leftovers are great
Easily multiplied but steaks should be about 1½lbs

1 tsp grapeseed oil
1½ lbs/700g small crimini mushrooms (halved)
1 cup shallots (finely chopped)
6 Tbl cognac
¾ cup non-fat beef stock
⅛ tsp salt
2 Tbl maple syrup
fresh ground black pepper to taste
1 Tbl unsalted butter
1½ lbs/700g lean London broil (top round)
⅛ tsp salt

Preheat the oven to 400°F/205°C and in it heat a large non-stick frying pan for about 10 minutes.

Remove; add the oil, swirling to coat the pan well. Add mushrooms and shallots.

Toss until well blended and return to the oven. Check the mushrooms about every 5 minutes, stirring with a wooden spatula if necessary. After about 15 minutes the mushrooms will be well browned. Add cognac, beef stock, salt, maple syrup, pepper and butter. Toss well and return to oven. Cook a further 10 minutes to reduce the liquid by half. Remove and set aside.

Place a large non-stick frying pan in the oven and heat for about 10 minutes. Sprinkle ½ of the salt across the top of the steak. Grind black pepper across the top. Place the steak seasoned side down in the hot pan and return to the oven. Before turning the steak sprinkle the remaining salt over the top. Rare steak takes about 8 minutes for the first side and 6 minutes after the turn. Medium-rare steak takes about 12 minutes for the first side and 8 minutes after the turn. Remove the steak from the oven, and allow it to rest on a board for 3–5 minutes. While the steak is resting return the mushrooms to the oven and turn it off. Carve the steak thinly across the grain. Divide the steak between 6 plates, top each with an equal portion of the mushrooms.

29

Maple Herb Crusted Rib Eye

Calories 224

Calories from Fat 81

Total Fat 9g (14%)

Saturated Fat 4g (20%)

Cholesterol 67mg (22%)

Sodium 366mg (15%)

Total Carbohydrates 10g (3%)

Dietary Fibre 0g (0%)

Protein 23g

Vitamin A (6%)

Vitamin C (10%)

Calcium (3%)

Iron (16%)

Dr. Tim says...

No matter what cut of beef is chosen, trimming the excess fat is the key to lowering fat and calories. A cut like rib eye steak that is not trimmed will have about 20g of fat per serving. Removing the excess fat will reduce the fat by 10g and about 90 calories. The best flavour in beef comes from the marbling in the meat itself, not the fat that surrounds the cut of meat. Choose cuts that have little excess fat and light marbling for maximum flavour and minimum calories.

Oregano

Maple syrup is a great choice for all types of cooking

Chef Tim says...

Maple syrup is a great choice for all types of cooking. It adds a rich, sweet, caramelized flavour to recipes like this steak. Used carefully it can help reduce the amount of fat and calories in a recipe. Like fat, it helps distribute flavours throughout the mouth.

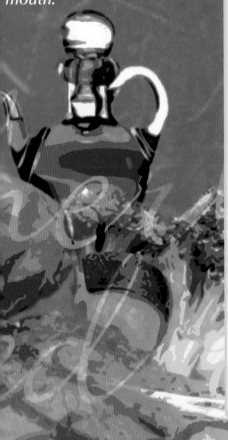

Serves 4
Serving size = ¼ lb/113g steak
Eat immediately, does not keep well
Easily multiplied by 2, 3 or 4

4 Tbl curly parsley (finely chopped)
3 Tbl oregano (finely chopped)
3 Tbl chives (finely chopped)
3 Tbl tarragon (finely chopped)
3 Tbl rosemary (finely chopped)
3 Tbl maple syrup
½ tsp salt
½ tsp fresh ground black pepper
4 x ¼ lb/113g rib eye steaks (small end - well trimmed)
Olive oil spray

Preheat the oven to 450°F/230°C and in it preheat a large non-stick frying pan for about 10 minutes. Put the finely chopped herbs together on a plate and the maple syrup on another plate. Sprinkle both sides of the steaks with salt and pepper. Dip one side of the steak in the maple syrup and then the other. Dip the coated steak in the herbs, turning to coat completely. Pat the herbs in place. If there is left over maple syrup or herbs, recoat the steaks. Remove the hot pan from the oven and spray lightly with oil. Immediately add the steaks to the hot pan so that they sear well. Return the pan to the oven and cook for about 4 minutes on the first side. Turn the steak to sear the other side and return to the oven. Cook on the second side for about 6 minutes for rare, 8 for medium-rare and 12 minutes for medium.

30

Fillet of Tenderloin with Roasted Pepper & Blue Cheese Sauce

...a simple and fast recipe...

For the 2 Tbl of the sauce alone:

Calories 28
Calories from Fat 18
Total Fat 2g (3%)
Saturated Fat 1g (5%)
Cholesterol 5mg (2%)
Sodium 244mg (10%)
Total Carbohydrates 1g (<1%)
Dietary Fibre <1g (0%)
Protein 2g
Vitamin A (15%)
Vitamin C (40%)
Calcium (4%)
Iron (<1%)

Calories 220
Calories from Fat 108
Total Fat 12g (18%)
Saturated Fat 5g (25%)
Cholesterol 75mg (25%)
Sodium 305mg (13%)
Total Carbohydrates 1g (<1%)
Dietary Fibre <1g (0%)
Protein 25g
Vitamin A (15%)
Vitamin C (40%)
Calcium (5%)
Iron (18%)

Chef Tim says...

This is a simple and fast recipe with ingredients that keep well around the house. Using ingredients from the healthy pantry list such as bottled roasted red peppers (get the ones that are packed in water and not oil) and blue cheese, it's nothing to whiz them together with a bit of pepper for the most sublime sauce. The sauce alone goes so well on so many things.

Dr. Tim says...

There are myriad varieties of blue cheeses. Most on the market are made from cow's milk but there are both sheep's and goat's milk versions as well.

Blue cheeses are generally a medium-fat cheese, having between 8 and 9g of fat per oz. Some are higher in fat with up to 12g per oz but, as with so many flavourful cheeses, a little goes a long way. Blue cheeses have a fair amount of sodium so you may not have to add salt to recipes that use blue cheese.

1oz blue cheese = 100 calories, 8g fat, 5g sat fat, 2g mono fat, 6g protein, <1g carbohydrates, 395mg sodium, 21mg cholesterol

Serves 4
Serving size = 2 Tbl sauce and ¼ lb/113g beef
The sauce will keep well for about 3 days in the refrigerator
Easily multiplied by 2, 3 or 4

½ cup roasted red pepper (finely chopped)
1oz/28g blue cheese
¼ tsp salt
⅛ tsp fresh ground black pepper
spray olive oil
4 x ¼ lb/113g fillet steaks

Make a sauce by blending the peppers and blue cheese until smooth. Add the salt and ground black pepper. In a pan gently heat the sauce on low. Preheat the oven to 450°F/230°C and place a large non-stick frying pan inside.

After about 10 minutes remove it and lightly spray with olive oil. Place the 4 fillets in the pan so that they do not touch, then return to the oven. Cook for about 5–7 minutes on each side for medium-rare. Serve topped with 2 Tbl sauce.

31

Beef Stew

Calories 256
Calories from Fat 81
Total Fat 7g (11%)
Saturated Fat 3g (15%)
Cholesterol 43mg (14%)
Sodium 397mg (17%)
Total Carbohydrates 27g (9%)
Dietary Fibre 4g (16%)
Protein 21g
Vitamin A (318%)
Vitamin C (42%)
Calcium (3%)
Iron (18%)

Dr. Tim says...

Cholesterol is essential for your body to produce steroids. Humans make about 300mg of cholesterol per day, about what we need for the body to function properly. The cholesterol molecule needs to be linked with other fats, known as "lipid particles", so that the cholesterol can be easily transported throughout the body in the blood stream. There are several types of these lipids. Of these, low density lipoprotein (LDL) cholesterol is the bad guy. The good stuff is HDL, or high density lipoprotein cholesterol. Remember, high is good, low is bad. There are a lot of factors that affect a person's cholesterol profile. Genetics, exercise and smoking are factors, but so is diet. Eating a diet that is high in saturated fat such as that found in animal products, or trans-fatty acid fats such as those found in margarines, increases the 'bad' LDL cholesterol.

Chef Tim says...

Don't stir stews too often or boil too fast, as the potatoes will break down. Gently stir the stew, at most about every 15 minutes. Parsnips are sweeter and make a great alternative to carrots in recipes, being both fantastic roasted or mashed.

¼ lb/113g parsnips = 85 calories, 0g fat, 0g sat fat, 0g mono fat, 1g protein, 20g carbohydrates, 11mg sodium, 0mg cholesterol

The most remarkable thing about my mother is that for thirty years she served the family nothing but leftovers. The original meal has never been found.

Calvin Trillin, author

Serves 8

Serving size = 2 cups

Leftovers are better than fresh

Keeps well for about 4 days in the fridge

Do not multiply

4 cups water
25 pearl onions (peeled)
⅓ cup all-purpose flour
1 tsp salt
¼ tsp ground black pepper
1½ lbs/700g flank steak
(¾ inch cubes)
cooking spray
½lb/225g fresh button mushrooms (quartered)
1 cup white onion (sliced)
1 Tbl lemon juice
1 Tbl Worcestershire sauce
1lb/450g carrots (peeled & sliced ¼ inch thick)
2 bay leaves
1½ lbs/700g red potatoes (peeled and ¾ inch cubes)
⅛ tsp ground allspice
4 cups water

In a small pan blanche the pearl onions in the water for about 10 minutes. Drain and place in a large stew pan. Preheat the oven to 400°F/205°C. Mix the flour, salt and pepper in a paper bag. Toss the cubes of flank steak in the flour, coating well. Coat a large non-stick frying pan with cooking spray and heat over a medium-high heat. Add meat and cook, turning until all sides are brown. Do not allow the cubes of beef to touch each other or the meat will steam and not brown. Add the meat to a large stew pot as it browns. Spray the hot pan with the cooking spray and add the mushrooms. Cook, stirring frequently, until browned. Then use the same frying pan to brown the onions until they are soft. Add them to the pot. Use the lemon juice and Worcestershire sauce to 'rinse' out the frying pan, scraping up anything stuck to the bottom. Add this liquid to the stew. Then add carrots, bay leaves, potatoes, allspice and water. Cover and place in the oven for 1 hour, stirring gently every 15 minutes.

32

Ginger Coriander Flank Steak

Calories 230
Calories from Fat 108
Total Fat 12g (18%)
Saturated Fat 4g (20%)
Cholesterol 57mg (19%)
Sodium 345mg (14%)
Total Carbohydrates 4g (1%)
Dietary Fibre 0g (0%)
Protein 23g
Vitamin A (4%)
Vitamin C (<1%)
Calcium (<1%)
Iron (13%)

Dr. Tim says...

There are 5 types of receptors on the tongue that sense all of the flavours that we taste. They are sour, salt, sweet, bitter, and one called umami (this was identified only about 6 years ago and is best described as savoury). Each of these flavours acts on their own but how they interact with each other is key to making recipes taste fantastic. Activation of one taste helps enhance another taste bud.

Sour
Sour tastes come from acidic foods. Because of the properties of acidic foods and how fast they react on the sour taste buds these flavours can quickly brighten an otherwise dull dish. The properties of salt react with acids and soften the bitterness of dishes. In doing so sweetness is enhanced.

Salt
Salty foods are obvious by themselves (like a salty pretzel) but just a little salt will enhance the other taste buds. Because it doesn't take very much, salt can be used in healthy cooking. Adding a little salt to something sweet, like chocolate, enhances the flavour of the chocolate.

Sweet
Sweet flavours stand on their own but they enhance other flavours also. Lemonade is a perfect example. Some people like bitter lemons but most like lemon flavour better if it has been sweetened.

Bitter
Bitter is not exactly sour. Bitter flavours would be those in a cabbage like radicchio.

Umami
Umami is the most interesting. Savoury foods like cheese, meat, mushrooms and tomatoes activate the umami taste buds. This flavour has been recognized by the Japanese for years. When umami flavours are combined, flavours are more than simply additive. Cheese and mushrooms together are more savoury than either of the two by themselves.

Chef Tim says...

To add flavour or to tenderize a food, it is often immersed in a seasoned liquid or marinade for a period of time. Most marinades are made with acidic ingredients (citrus juice, vinegar, wine, etc.) because the low pH helps break down foods.

The acids can also react with the container, so foods should be marinated in a non-reactive dish such as ceramic, glass or stainless steel, or in a sealed plastic bag.

Serves 4
Serving size = ¼ lb/113g beef
Leftovers make good sandwiches and salads
Steak keeps well in the refrigerator for about 3 days
To multiply, separate the bags of marinade with steak

1lb/450g flank steak
3 Tbl ginger (finely chopped)
1 Tbl dark sesame oil
1 Tbl low-sodium soy sauce
1 Tbl rice vinegar
1 Tbl Splenda sugar substitute
1 tsp red bean paste
½ cup fresh coriander leaves
spray oil

Combine the flank steak, ginger, sesame oil, soy sauce, rice vinegar, Splenda, red bean paste and coriander leaves in a sealed plastic bag or lidded box. Close and toss to coat the steak well. Leave to marinate at least 4 hours in the refrigerator or ideally overnight.

Preheat the grill or barbecue to medium-high heat. Lightly spray a grill pan with oil. Put the flank steak on the pan or barbecue and cook for about 8–9 minutes on each side for medium-rare. Remove to a cutting board and allow the meat to rest for about 5–10 minutes prior to slicing. Carve the meat as thinly as possible and serve.

33

Shiitake and Cranberry Stuffed Pork Loin

Calories 330

Calories from Fat 90

Total Fat 10g (15%)

Saturated Fat 3g (15%)

Cholesterol 62mg (21%)

Sodium 224mg (9%)

Total Carbohydrates 25g (8%)

Dietary Fibre 3g (10%)

Protein 30g

Vitamin A (67%)

Vitamin C (15%)

Calcium (3%)

Iron (20%)

Dr. Tim says...

This recipe calls for dried cranberries. Many dried cranberries have been sweetened with sugar. A ⅓ cup of dried cranberries is 120 calories, whereas a cup of fresh is only 47 calories. ⅓ cup of dried fruit has about 4 teaspoons of added sugar. Added sweetness does change their character and adds a chewy texture that fresh cranberries don't have. Note the difference in serving size and calories between dried and fresh:

⅓ cup dried cranberries = 120 calories, 0g fat, 0g sat fat, 0g mono fat, 0g protein, 29g carbohydrates, 0mg sodium, 0mg cholesterol

1 cup fresh cranberries = 47 calories, 0g fat, 0g sat fat, 0g mono fat, 0g protein, 12g carbohydrates, 0mg sodium, 0mg cholesterol

you will know they are fresh if they bounce!

Chef Tim says...

Fresh cranberries are harvested in the autumn, beginning in September and reaching the market in early October. They are quite tart and are usually mixed with sweeter fruits or sugar before cooking, making for a wonderful balance in chutneys, sauces and stuffings. Fresh berries should not be wrinkled or soft. Because the ripe berries have a little air inside, you will know they are fresh if they bounce! Frozen cranberries make a reasonably good substitute for fresh.

Serves 6

Serving size = ¼lb/113g pork

Leftovers make great sandwiches and any re-heating should be gentle

Easily multiplied by 2 or 3

---

2 tsp grapeseed oil
2½ lbs/1.1kg shiitake mushrooms (thinly sliced)
2 large (1 cup) shallots (finely chopped)
¼ cup dried cranberries
¼ cup tawny port
½ cup chicken stock
¼ tsp salt
fresh ground black pepper to taste
1 Tbl maple syrup
1 Tbl fresh rosemary leaves
1½ lb/700g pork loin (well trimmed)
¼ cup tawny port
½ cup chicken stock
½ cup water
2 tsp cornflour
olive oil spray

Stuffing

First make the stuffing by heating half the oil in a large non-stick frying pan on a medium heat. Add mushrooms and sauté, tossing frequently, until a dark roasted brown. Heat the other half of the oil in a medium frying pan. Add the shallots; stir gently until soft and translucent. Add cranberries, port, chicken stock, salt, pepper and maple syrup. Increase the heat slightly and cook until all but about 1 Tbl of the liquid has evaporated. Remove from heat and set aside. Fold the cooked mushrooms into the cranberry mixture. Add the rosemary and toss until well blended. Refrigerate for at least 30 minutes.

Roast

Preheat the oven to 400°F/205°C. Place a large non-stick frying pan in the oven. While it is heating, trim the outside of the pork of all excess fat. Slice the meat open lengthwise, so it opens like a book. Place about half of the stuffing inside and roll up like a giant sausage and truss with loops of cotton at 5 equal intervals. Spray lightly with olive oil and add the pork loin to the pan to sear. Return to the oven and turn about every 4 minutes for the first 15 minutes or so to sear the outside well. Leave to roast for 45 minutes or until a probe shows an internal temperature of 160°F/70°C.

Sauce

Place the remaining cranberry/shiitake mixture, the tawny port and a ¼ cup chicken stock in a stainless steel or enamel-lined pan, on medium heat. Simmer, then reduce to medium-low. As the sauce reduces, add the water about 2 Tbl at a time. Blend 2 tsp of cornflour in the remaining ¼ cup chicken stock. Remove the roast from the oven and set it on a board to rest. Increase the heat under the sauce to medium and add the cornflour/chicken stock mixture. Stir until thickened. Slice the pork loin into 6 slices of equal thickness. Remove the trussing twine as you slice. Serve topped with sauce.

34

Lemon Pork with Lentils

Calories 441
Calories from Fat 108
Total Fat 12g (24%)
Saturated Fat 3g (15%)
Cholesterol 74mg (25%)
Sodium 287mg (12%)
Total Carbohydrates 37g (12%)
Dietary Fibre 15g (60%)
Protein 38g
Vitamin A (28%)
Vitamin C (19%)
Calcium (6%)
Iron (31%)

Dr. Tim says...

Trimming beef, lamb and pork of fat, reduces calories simply by lowering the amount of fat. From a health standpoint this is key, because there is clear proof that consuming fewer calories in the form of saturated fat lowers the risk of heart attack and stroke.

There is not much cholesterol in the fat, though. It is found in the meat itself. So the amount of cholesterol is fairly similar in most cuts of meat. Each oz of red meat has about 25mg of cholesterol.

Chef Tim says...

Lentils are legumes like peas and peanuts and can be cooked whole, but because of their size lentils don't have to be soaked overnight like other legumes. They break down quickly, so are great in making soups and sauces thick and creamy.

They are mostly carbohydrate and protein, not very much fat.

They have tons of fibre with ½ cup of cooked lentils coming in at around 8g.

2oz/57g lentils = 192 calories, <1g fat, 0g sat fat, 0g mono fat, 16g protein, 32g carbohydrates, 6mg sodium, 0mg cholesterol

Serves 4
Serving size = 1 pork chop with about ½ cup cooked lentils
Serve immediately
Easily multiplied by 2

1 Tbl extra virgin olive oil
2 Tbl fresh lemon juice plus zest of one lemon
1 Tbl pure maple syrup
1 Tbl curly parsley (chopped)
2 Tbl fresh rosemary
1 clove garlic (crushed)
4 x ¼lb/113g centre cut pork chops
½ cup red lentils
½ cup green lentils
6 cups water
1 tsp extra virgin olive oil
1 shallot (finely chopped)
1 rib celery (diced)
¼ tsp red pepper flakes
¼ cup dry sherry
¼ tsp salt
1 tsp unsalted butter
¼ cup dry sherry
¼ tsp salt

Place the olive oil, lemon juice, lemon zest, maple syrup, parsley, rosemary, garlic clove and pork chops in a sealed plastic bag and refrigerate overnight. Cook the red and green lentils separately, each in 3 cups of simmering water for about 15–20 minutes until just tender. Drain and rinse with cold water. The lentils can be done in advance and refrigerated until needed. Preheat oven to 350°F/175°C. Heat a large non-stick frying pan on medium-high. Sear the chops for about 2 minutes on each side and add the marinade. Place the pan in the oven.

While the chops are cooking, heat 1 tsp of olive oil in a medium non-stick frying pan on medium high. Add the shallot, celery and pepper and reduce the heat, cooking 3–4 minutes until soft. Add the cooked lentils and toss until warmed through. Add the first ¼ cup sherry and ¼ tsp salt. Reduce by about half (about 2 minutes). Add the butter and swirl.

Set the heat on low until the pork is cooked (about 20 minutes). Divide the lentils between 4 warmed plates. Remove the pork chops from the pan and place one on each plate. Discard the garlic from the marinade in the frying pan and increase the heat to medium high. 'Rinse' the pan with the second ¼ cup of sherry and ¼ tsp of salt and reduce by half, pouring the sauce evenly over each pork chop.

35

Grilled Sage Lamb Kebab

Lamb Info (¼lb/113g portion)	Calories	Fat g	Sodium mg	Saturated Fat g	Cholesterol mg	Mono-unsaturated Fat g	Poly-unsaturated Fat g
Chump chops	192	10.4	82	3.7	75	4.2	0.95
Loin chops	162	6.7	77	2.4	75	2.7	0.61
Leg	145	5.1	70	1.8	73	2.0	0.46
Shoulder	163	7.7	79	2.7	75	3.1	0.70

Calories 419
Calories from Fat 117
Total Fat 13g (19%)
Saturated Fat 3g (15%)
Cholesterol 75mg (25%)
Sodium 385mg (16%)
Total Carbohydrates 48g (16%)
Dietary Fibre 6g (19%)
Protein 26g
Vitamin A (80%)
Vitamin C (279%)
Calcium (5%)
Iron (25%)

Dr. Tim says...

There are a couple of concerns amongst scientists about grilling meats to the point where the edges are charred black. The short answer is that we don't know if this is harmful. One concern is about the fat dripping onto hot charcoal and the forming of PAHs (polycyclic aromatic hydrocarbons) – basically soot. Some associations with cancer have been shown but grilling has not been proven to be a problem. The other issue concerns pan-searing or broiling meats. Heterocyclic Amines (or HAs) can form which may be harmful, but about which little is known. A little bit of char every once in a while probably won't do much harm.

grilled

Chef Tim says...

Lamb has only a little more fat than pork and is often leaner than beef. A ¼lb/113g serving averages 170 calories and 6g of fat. That compares well with beef tenderloin at 180 calories and 9g of fat. As with all red meats, look for leaner cuts. This is easy with lamb because most cuts are only lightly marbled and excess fat is easily trimmed.

Serves 2
Serving size = 1 kebab
Marinade keeps well overnight in the refrigerator
Easily multiplied by any amount

2 Tbl fresh sage
2 Tbl fresh parsley
2 Tbl fresh chives
1 Tbl fresh lemon juice
1 Tbl pure maple syrup
2 Tbl sherry
1 Tbl extra virgin olive oil
1 Tbl dark brown sugar
¼ tsp salt
½ lb/225g lamb shoulder (lean)
2 cups water
4 medium red or Yukon gold potatoes (halved)
½ medium white onion (peeled and halved)
½ red pepper (quartered)
6 shiitake mushroom caps

Blend together the sage, parsley, chives, lemon juice, maple syrup, sherry, olive oil, brown sugar and salt until smooth. Cut the lamb into 8 1oz cubes. Add to the marinade and refrigerate in a bag or lidded box for at least 4 hours or ideally overnight. Steam the potatoes and the ½ onion over the water for 15 minutes. Allow to cool. Quarter the rest of the onion and lace skewers alternately with mushrooms, lamb, onion, pepper and potato. Keep the marinade in reserve. Cook the kebabs over a hot grill. Turn about every 3 minutes and baste with the remaining marinade as they cook, about 15–20 minutes in all.

36

Caribbean Shrimp

Calories	180
Calories from Fat	63
Total Fat 7g	(11%)
Saturated Fat 1g	(4%)
Cholesterol 172mg	(57%)
Sodium 277mg	(12%)
Total Carbohydrates 6g	(2%)
Dietary Fibre <1g	(0%)
Protein 23g	
Vitamin A	(17%)
Vitamin C	(31%)
Calcium	(6%)
Iron	(50%)

Dr. Tim says...

A study published in 1990 in the Journal of Arteriosclerosis showed a remarkably beneficial effect of grapeseed oil. It appears that one ounce per day is enough, with the research showing a 13–14% increase in the HDL or "good cholesterol". In another study published in the Journal of the American College of Cardiology, 56 participants with low 'good' levels substituted up to 1½oz of grapeseed oil for the oil they usually used in recipes. At the end of the study the subjects showed no significant change in weight or total cholesterol, but the ratio of 'bad' to 'good' had changed, with a 7% reduction in 'bad' and a 13% increase in 'good' levels.

Chef Tim says...

Most shrimp sold has been frozen, but freezing doesn't affect the flavour as much as with other fish. They are sold by size, and the grading system (that isn't very accurate) is based on the number of shrimp per pound. Small shrimp will have 36–45 per pound, medium 31–35, large 21–30, extra large 16–20 and jumbo, which are 11–15 per pound. Colossal shrimp (less than 10 shrimp per pound) are often referred to as prawns, although prawns are actually a different species. Note the sodium content of shrimp:

¼lb/113g shrimp = 120 calories, 2g fat, 0g sat fat, 0g mono fat, 23g protein, 1g carbohydrates, 167mg sodium, 172mg cholesterol

Serves 2
Serving size = ¼lb/113g shrimp and ¼ cup melon salsa
Leftovers are great in sandwiches and salads
Easily multiplied by 2, 3 or 4

½lb/225g large shrimp (peeled & deveined)
2 tsp grapeseed oil
1 Tbl fresh lime juice
2 tsp jerk seasoning blend, see next recipe
2 lime wedges
½ cup melon or mango salsa, see recipe after next
4 Tbl coriander leaves

Preheat the barbecue or grill to medium heat. Mix the shrimp, grapeseed oil, lime juice and jerk seasoning together and let stand for at least 10 minutes. Thread the shrimp onto metal or wooden skewers. Grill for about 2 minutes on the first side and then turn. Cook until opaque in the centre. Brush frequently with marinade. Total cooking time about 5–7 minutes. Serve with melon or mango salsa. Top with fresh coriander leaves and garnish with lime wedges.

37

Jerk Rub

Calories 2

Calories from Fat 0

Total Fat 0g (0%)

Saturated Fat 0g (0%)

Cholesterol 0mg (0%)

Sodium 97mg (4%)

Total Carbohydrates <1g (<1%)

Dietary Fibre 0g (0%)

Protein 0g

Vitamin A (0%)

Vitamin C (0%)

Calcium (0%)

Iron (0%)

Dr. Tim says...

There is no significant nutritional difference between granulated sugar and brown sugar. Most brown sugars are made by combining sugar with molasses. This determines the darkness of the sugar. Light brown sugar has a more delicate flavour and recipes in this book generally use light brown sugar unless specified otherwise.

1 Tbl = 34 calories, 0g fat, 0g sat fat, 0g mono fat, 0g protein, 9g carbohydrates, 4mg sodium, 0mg cholesterol

...ubiquitous in the Caribbean islands...

Chef Tim says...

Jerk rubs are ubiquitous in the Caribbean islands. There are as many different recipes for jerk as there are for chutney.

Core ingredients are spring onions, allspice, thyme, black pepper, nutmeg and cinnamon.

The traditional chilli used is a Scotch bonnet. This is a fabulously hot pepper – handle it with respect. There are both dry jerk rubs and wet jerk rubs. The latter is often made from oil, rum, whisky, honey or molasses to create a sticky sauce that is used as a marinade, and is spread on while grilling.

Serves 24
Serving size = 1 tsp
Keeps well in a sealed container for up to 6 months
Makes ½ cup

1 small dried chilli
1 Tbl black peppercorns
1 Tbl onion powder
2 tsp allspice
2 tsp cinnamon
½ tsp ground cumin

1 Tbl coriander seeds
1 Tbl garlic powder
1 Tbl ground ginger
1 Tbl thyme
½ tsp nutmeg
1 Tbl light brown sugar
½ tsp whole cloves
1 tsp salt

Combine all ingredients in a blender until powdered.

38

Mango or Melon Salsa

Calories 28
Calories from Fat 0
Total Fat 0g (0%)
Saturated Fat 0g (0%)
Cholesterol 0mg (0%)
Sodium 0mg (0%)
Total Carbohydrates 7g (2%)
Dietary Fibre 0g (0%)
Protein 0g
Vitamin A (50%)
Vitamin C (38%)
Calcium (<1%)
Iron (<1%)

Dr. Tim says...

Scales are one of the most important pieces of equipment in healthy eating. Portion size is important – it doesn't work well to guess how much ¼lb/13g of fresh salmon fillet is (at least at first). An inexpensive set of scales will do. Make sure it measures in grams and in ounces.

Chef Tim says...

This salsa is a great example of using opposites. The mango is sweet and is balanced by the hot chilli powder. The coriander adds a fresh, pungent flavour, and the peppers a bit of tartness. If serving with less salty foods, add just a touch – ⅛ to ¼ tsp at most, or a dash of lime if served with less acidic foods.

Another good example of opposite flavours creating balance in recipes is strawberries with balsamic vinegar and fresh ground black pepper. While these three don't seem to go together they complement each other perfectly by stimulating the taste buds in perfect harmony.

Serves 6
Serving size = ½ cup
This salsa keeps for about 3 days in the fridge if tightly covered
Easily multiplied by 2, 3 or 4

1½ cups mango or cantaloupe melon
1 tsp chilli powder
2 Tbl fresh coriander leaves
1 Tbl red pepper (diced)
1 Tbl green pepper (diced)

Peel and cut the mango or melon into small dice-sized chunks or use a food processor for the same result. Mix in the chilli powder, coriander and half of each of the peppers. Fold by hand until the pepper is blended in. Fold in the remaining diced peppers. Chill well.

savouries

"This salsa is a great example of using opposites"

39

Pizza Dough

Calories 289
Calories from Fat 9
Total Fat 1g (5%)
Saturated Fat 0g (0%)
Cholesterol 0mg (0%)
Sodium 292mg (12%)
Total Carbohydrates 60g (20%)
Dietary Fibre 2g (8%)
Protein 8g
Vitamin A (0%)
Vitamin C (0%)
Calcium (1%)
Iron (21%)

Dr. Tim says...

As mentioned elsewhere, baking is essentially a science, much like working with a chemistry set. Exact measurements are important because of how a little more leavening agent or moisture can affect the finished product.

The problem is that all of this can also be affected by the ingredients themselves. For instance, the moisture content in flours varies greatly. Not only is this different between different manufacturers of flours, but flour also loses moisture during storage.

As you knead or mix flour it will pick up moisture. If it is a humid day you may actually need slightly more flour. Or, if your flour has been stored for a long time, you may need less because of the lower moisture content. So maybe in the end, baking is an art?

...maybe in the en

Chef Tim says...

Pizza dough doesn't store very well. If more is made than needed, and saving it for the next day is the plan, wrap it immediately in cling film, like a sweet, with the ends twisted tightly, and store in the coldest part of the fridge.

...ing is an art?

Serves 4

Serving size = 1 individual pizza (¼ recipe)

Will keep for about 36 hours refrigerated if well sealed

Easily multiplied or divided by 2

1 cup warm water
1 tsp dry active yeast
1 tsp sugar
2½ cups all-purpose flour
½ tsp salt

Heat the water until warm to touch – about 110°F–115°F (43°C–46°C). If the water is too hot it will kill the yeast. Add to the yeast and sugar in a large mixing bowl. Stir until well blended. Let the mixture stand for about 5–7 minutes until foamy.

Add the flour and salt and stir with a fork until a coarse dough forms.

Continue to mix by hand until a dough ball forms. Cover the bowl and keep it warm in about 4 inches of hot water. This will help the dough rise. The dough will double in size in about 30–40 minutes.

Punch it a few times with your fingers and let it rise another 30 minutes. Cut the ball into four equal pieces. Cover the dough that you are not going to use immediately in plastic wrap, then chill.

FLOUR

40

Pizza - Dill Pesto and Potato

Calories 453

Calories from Fat 99

Total Fat 11g (17%)

Saturated Fat 3g (15%)

Cholesterol 12mg (4%)

Sodium 454mg (19%)

Total Carbohydrates 73g (24%)

Dietary Fibre 3g (12%)

Protein 16g

Vitamin A (11%)

Vitamin C (29%)

Calcium (19%)

Iron (28%)

Dr. Tim says...

If you are going to make pizza regularly (and you should – it's really healthy) then buy a pizza stone. These come in both round and rectangular shapes and are made with everything from ceramic or clay to different mixtures of cement. The latter appears to be more durable (I have broken more than a few ceramic pizza stones).

Place the stone in a cold oven and set the temperature to top heat. It will take about 20 minutes to heat the oven and stone together. I generally place my shaped pizza dough directly on the stone and then add the toppings. You can use a peel (the large paddle you see in pizza restaurants) and assemble the pizza prior to sliding it onto the stone.

The heat will be transferred evenly to your pizza, crisping the crust. Over time the stone will darken. When you are done, simply shut off the oven and let the stone cool. I don't use water on mine, but simply brush it off or use a spatula to scrape off anything that has stuck to the stone.

Chef Tim says...

Mozzarella is one of the cheeses the Italians call pasta filata – cheeses that have been scalded and kneaded prior to ageing. Ricotta and provolone are also pasta filata cheeses. Originally made in Naples from the rich milk of water buffaloes, the cheese available outside of Italy labelled "mozzarella" can be made from any type of milk. The most familiar mozzarella is the low-moisture version. It is a moist cheese with a rubbery quality that melts exceptionally well, making it ideal for pizza. High-moisture mozzarella is often called "fresh". It is soft with a sublime taste.

1oz/28g mozzarella = 72 calories, 4.5g fat, 3g salt, 1g mono fat, 7g protein, 0g carbohydrates, 132mg sodium, 16mg cholesterol

Serves 1
Serving size = 1 pizza
Leftovers are good cold for breakfast the next morning
Easily multiplied by 2, 3 or 4

1 litre water
2 small red potatoes
2 Tbl dill pesto (next recipe)
½oz fresh mozzarella (cut into small dice)
½ pizza dough recipe from previous pages
fresh ground pepper to taste

Boil the water in a pan over high heat and add the potatoes. Cook until tender. Remove and cool. Slice into rounds about ¼ inch thick.

Preheat a pizza stone or baking tray in a 500°F/260°C oven. Gently stretch the dough into a round shape. Don't work too hard to get it perfect. Once the dough is formed place the pizza dough on a floured cutting board and spread the pesto over the dough. Top with slices of potato and sprinkle with the mozzarella and add pepper to taste. Slide onto the heated pizza stone or baking tray and bake for about 12–15 minutes until the crust is golden brown.

"It is soft with a sublime taste"

41

Dill Pesto

Calories 83

Calories from Fat 72

Total Fat 8g (12%)

Saturated Fat 2g (8%)

Cholesterol 19mg (6%)

Sodium 92mg (4%)

Total Carbohydrates 2g (<1%)

Dietary Fibre 0g (0%)

Protein 3g

Vitamin A (12%)

Vitamin C (14%)

Calcium (6%)

Iron (5%)

Dr. Tim says...

The fats we eat are made of fatty acids. These are simply long chains of carbon atoms, with each carbon atom on the chain having 2 hydrogen atoms hanging from it. 3 fatty acid chains are attached to a 4th molecule called glycerol and the result is the fat that we eat. Fats are considered to be saturated when every carbon atom has 2 hydrogen atoms hanging off it. Some fats are less saturated than others. When there is 1 pair of hydrogen atoms missing the fat is called monounsaturated, and when more than 1 pair is missing it is known as polyunsaturated.

When the polyunsaturated fat is kinked in a particular way it is known as a trans-fatty acid. Polyunsaturated fats that are high in trans-fatty acids have been shown to be as bad for you as saturated fats.

When the hydrogen atoms are missing at the 3rd place from the end of the chain the fatty acid is known as an Omega-3 fatty acid. These types of fats are found in high concentrations in many fish and have been shown to prevent heart disease.

Pine nuts, like all seeds and nuts, are high in fat. A teaspoon has 5g of fat but, also like most seeds and nuts, the majority of the fat is mono-unsaturated fat (2g of mono-unsaturated and 2g of poly-unsaturated fat in a teaspoon).

1oz/28g pine nuts = 146 calories, 14g fat, 2g sat fat, 5g mono fat, 7g protein, 4g carbohydrates, 1mg sodium, 0mg cholesterol

Chef Tim says...

Fresh lemons keep fairly well in the fridge for about 2 weeks. The juice of 1 lemon varies greatly.

A large lemon can have as much as 4 Tbl of lemon juice but when a recipe calls for the juice of 1 lemon you never really know. Start with 2 Tbl and increase the amount for taste.

Serves 6
Serving size = 2 Tbl
Keeps well for up to a week in the refrigerator
Easily multiplied by 2

2 Tbl pine nuts
2 cloves garlic (finely chopped)
4 cups fresh dill

1oz/28g Parmigiano-Reggiano
Parmesan (grated)
2 Tbl water
2 tsp fresh lemon juice
2 Tbl extra virgin olive oil

Blend pine nuts, garlic fresh dill, Parmesan, water, lemon juice and olive oil until smooth. Chill thoroughly.

savouries

"Some fats are less saturated than others"

42

Pizza with Tomato, Basil and Garlic

Calories 468

Calories from Fat 90

Total Fat 10g (14%)

Saturated Fat 5g (25%)

Cholesterol 25mg (9%)

Sodium 695mg (29%)

Total Carbohydrates 71g (24%)

Dietary Fibre 4g (16%)

Protein 23g

Vitamin A (24%)

Vitamin C (56%)

Calcium (32%)

Iron (31%)

Dr. Tim says...

I look for good quality bottled sauces that have as few fat and calories as possible. The Paul Newman, Newman's Own brand is good and, although not widely available in the UK, there are so many lovely sauces that it is merely a matter of checking the nutritional information. I look for sauces that have 2g of fat or less per ½ cup. Do look carefully at the ingredients because many sauces have added sugar and, while this can add calories, the information can also be very important for diabetics.

Chef Tim says...

Buying tomatoes at the supermarket can be a daunting task. The quality is often poor because most are picked green and ripened in big rooms using ethylene gas. However, even the worst tomato can be made better by placing it stem side down on a sunny windowsill. It will continue to ripen further and if you want it chilled, place it in the fridge for just a couple of hours.

1 medium (¼lb/113g) tomato = 26 calories, 0.4g fat, <1g sat fat, <1g mono fat, 1g protein, 6g carbohydrates, 11mg sodium, 0mg cholesterol

Serves 1
Serving size = 1 pizza
Leftovers are good cold for breakfast the next morning
Easily multiplied by 2, 3 or 4

1 medium (¼lb/113g) tomato
1oz/28g fresh mozzarella
8 large fresh basil leaves, sliced into strips
4 cloves quartered roasted garlic, see Recipe 26
½oz/14g Parmigiano-Reggiano Parmesan (grated)
¼ pizza dough recipe as in Recipe 39

Preheat the oven to 500°F/260°C. Pizza is best baked on a pizza stone but a baking tray will work fairly well. Place the baking stone or tray in the oven and allow it to heat at least 15-20 minutes. Meanwhile slice the tomato in half vertically. Remove the seeds and slice the tomato into strips. Cut the fresh mozzarella into half-inch cubes. Gently toss the tomato strips, mozzarella, basil and garlic in a small bowl. Using a quarter of the pizza dough recipe (for each pizza), stretch into 8 inch rounds. Don't work too hard to get a perfectly round shape. Place it on the hot pizza stone and top with the tomato/mozzarella mixture. Bake for approximately 8 minutes, then top with the Parmesan cheese. Bake for another 3–5 minutes, until the cheese has melted. Remove from the oven and let it cool for about 90 seconds, slice and serve.

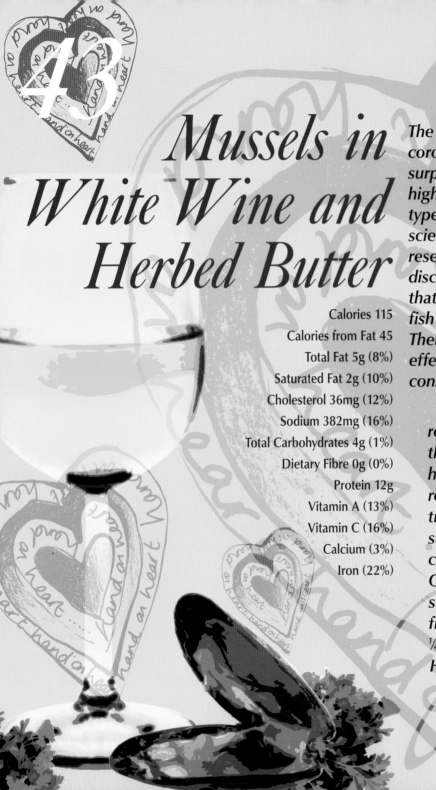

43

Mussels in White Wine and Herbed Butter

Calories 115
Calories from Fat 45
Total Fat 5g (8%)
Saturated Fat 2g (10%)
Cholesterol 36mg (12%)
Sodium 382mg (16%)
Total Carbohydrates 4g (1%)
Dietary Fibre 0g (0%)
Protein 12g
Vitamin A (13%)
Vitamin C (16%)
Calcium (3%)
Iron (22%)

Dr. Tim says...

The Inuit Eskimos have a low incidence of coronary heart disease, which is surprising, since the Eskimos also have a high-fat diet. The difference is that the types of fats they consume are fish oils, scientifically known as Omega-3 fats, which research shows reduce total cholesterol and discourage blood clotting. The consensus is that most people benefit from eating oily fish like tuna, salmon, mackerel and trout. There are many studies investigating the effects of supplements versus actual fish consumption.

The British Heart Foundation recommends supplements only for those few people who have extremely high triglycerides and who have not responded favourably to standard treatments. A study on fish oil supplements found that people could reap the benefits of Omega-3 oils by taking a 2g supplement per day. In actual fish terms, that equals about ¼lb/113g of salmon. Hmmm... The choice? Pills? Salmon? Pills? Salmon? I'll take the fish any day.

Chef Tim says...

Cook mussels the day they are bought by heating them in steaming liquid to a boil, until the shells are open fully, then serve immediately. If need be the fresh mussels can be stored overnight or longer in the bottom of the refrigerator inside a strainer set over a bowl.

Place some ice on top of the mussels and change it frequently to keep them as cold as possible. Because most mussels are now farmed on ropes they are not as likely to be gritty. They will often still have a "beard". These are the "byssal threads" that mussels use to anchor themselves. Remove it by pulling toward the hinge, not the open end of the mussel.

1lb/450g mussels in shell = 3½oz/100g shelled = 85 calories, 2g fat, <1g sat fat, <1g mono fat, 12g protein, 4g carbohydrates, 284mg sodium, 28mg cholesterol

Butter makes 8 servings
Serving size = 1lb mussels in shell and 1 Tbl herbed butter
The butter keeps well for up to 4 days refrigerated
Easily multiplied by 2 or 3

2 Tbl unsalted butter
2 Tbl shallots (finely chopped)
2 Tbl white onion (finely chopped)
2 Tbl curly parsley (finely chopped)
¼ cup (per serving) white wine

⅛ tsp (per serving) salt
1lb (per serving) mussels (cleaned)

Cream together the butter, shallot, onion and parsley. (Can be made the night before and refrigerated). Bring to the boil in a medium to large stainless steel or enamelled pan, ¼ cup white wine and ⅛ tsp salt with one 1Tbl of the "herbed butter" per serving.

Place 1 lb mussels (per serving) in the pan and cover. Steam until mussels are just opened, (3–5 minutes). Serve in bowl with broth.

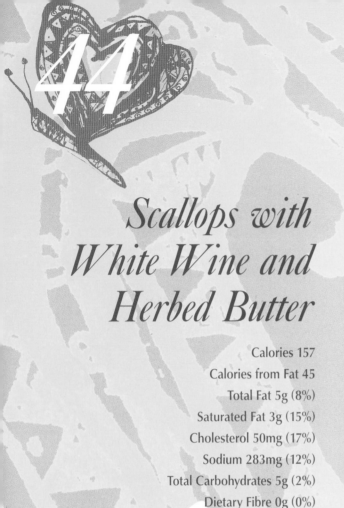

44

Scallops with White Wine and Herbed Butter

Calories 157
Calories from Fat 45
Total Fat 5g (8%)
Saturated Fat 3g (15%)
Cholesterol 50mg (17%)
Sodium 283mg (12%)
Total Carbohydrates 5g (2%)
Dietary Fibre 0g (0%)
Protein 19g
Vitamin A (16%)
Vitamin C (16%)
Calcium (4%)
Iron (3%)

Dr. Tim says...

A lot of these recipes use wine or other alcoholic beverages. During the cooking process most of the alcohol evaporates, but not completely.

Many people don't wish to use any alcohol and there are alternatives. There are good non-alcoholic wines on the market with some coming from better California vineyards. One brand that is relatively easy to find is Fré, www.frewines.com and is used by many chefs when they want to avoid alcohol. To replace rum or bourbon, use extracts that have similar flavours, although they do still contain a trace of alcohol.

Keep in mind that in 1 Tbl of wine there's not a lot of alcohol to start with. There's less than ½ teaspoon of alcohol in 1 Tbl of wine. Alcohol evaporates faster than the water in the wine, but there will still be a little alcohol left after cooking.

The amount that remains depends on what is being cooked. A stew like beef bourguignon, that cooks for a few hours, will have time for more of the alcohol to burn off. On the other hand, in a dish that is rapidly cooked, like this scallop recipe, as much as 50% of the alcohol may remain. So there could be as much as ¼ teaspoon of alcohol in a serving.

Chef Tim says...

When cooking any recipe with scallops make sure that any other accompanying recipes are finished first. Begin the scallop recipe and watch the scallops carefully. They will begin to firm up the second that they are hot and when fully cooked they should have a slight rubbery give when pinched. Cooked too long and they will quickly turn into little chewy rubber bullets.

Serves 2 (enough butter for 8 servings)
Serving size = ¼lb/113g scallops and 2 Tbl butter
The herbed butter keeps well for about 4–5 days tightly covered in the refrigerator
Easily multiplied by 2

3 Tbl unsalted butter (softened)
1½ tsp garlic (finely chopped)
3 Tbl shallot (finely chopped)
5 Tbl fresh curly parsley (finely chopped)
1 Tbl fresh dill
3 Tbl fresh lemon juice

2 Tbl dry sherry
½lb/226g fresh scallops
4 Tbl white table wine

Blend the butter, garlic, shallot, parsley, dill, lemon juice and sherry in a mixing bowl. Preheat the oven to 325°F/162°C. Place ¼/113g portions of scallops in individual or au gratin dishes. Add 2 Tbl of herbed butter to each dish. Add 2 Tbl of wine to each dish. Place in the pre-heated oven and cook until the scallops are done – about 12–15 minutes (this will be when they turn milky white but are still slightly tender to the touch).

45

Soy Mustard Scallops

Calories 182
Calories from Fat 36
Total Fat 4g (6%)
Saturated Fat <1g (2%)
Cholesterol 37mg (12%)
Sodium 774mg (32%)
Total Carbohydrates 12g (4%)
Dietary Fibre 1g (4%)
Protein 21g
Vitamin A (12%)
Vitamin C (90%)
Calcium (15%)
Iron (8%)

Dr. Tim says...

Non-stick pans are essential to healthy cooking and a good quality pan that is made with a slightly porous metal is one of the best non-stick pans you can buy. The iron skillet is a good example. Aluminium is another good choice because it heats evenly and is fairly responsive to changes in heat. But pans like these have to be cured, and care must be taken when using soap as it will wash away the oil used to cure the pan.

Pans made with porous metals, such as iron or aluminium, can oxidize while acidic foods are cooking and discolour foods. There are many excellent quality pots and pans with non-stick coatings on the market now.

Chef Tim says...

Sea scallops are about 1½ inches in diameter and should be a translucent beige, creamy colour. Some will be slightly pink. Because scallops don't live as well out of water as clams or oysters, they are shucked when caught and kept chilled on board the fishing boat.

For years many scallops have been treated with sodium tripolyphosphate (STP) which helps to retain the natural moisture but results in excess absorption of water. This can increase the weight by as much as 25% and makes for a damp, gummy scallop. The STP-treated scallops take on a white, opaque appearance and have a bitter chemical flavour. Look for scallops labelled "chemical free" or "dry pack".

¼lb/113g sea scallops = 100 calories, <1g fat, 0g sat fat, 0g mono fat, 19g protein, 3g carbohydrates, 182mg sodium, 37mg cholesterol

Serves 2
Serving size = ¼lb/113g scallops
Doesn't keep well
Easily multiplied by 2 using a larger pan

1 cup chicken stock
1 Tbl Chinese or hot mustard
1 Tbl pure maple syrup
½ tsp wasabi paste
½ Tbl soy sauce
1 cup water (for steaming pak choy)
2 baby pak choy
1 litre ice water
1 tsp dark sesame oil
½lb/225g fresh sea scallops
¼ tsp black sesame seeds
2 Tbl fresh coriander leaves

In a small stainless or enamelled pan boil the chicken stock, mustard, maple syrup, wasabi paste and soy sauce on high heat. Simmer, reducing the sauce by half, and remove from the heat.

Prepare an ice bath for the pak choy using ice cubes in a bowl filled with water. Steam the pak choy for about 2 minutes, remove and place them in the ice water bath to stop them from cooking further. After they are cool, drain completely and slice in half lengthwise. Preheat the oven to a warm setting. Heat the sesame oil on high in a large frying pan.

When the oil is nearly smoking place the scallops in the pan so they don't touch each other. Sear on the first side for about 3 minutes and turn. Cook for another 2–3 minutes. Remove to a plate and keep in a warm oven. Place the pak choy in the same pan and sear for about 1 minute on the cut side.

Turn and add the sauce and cook for about 30 seconds. Arrange scallops and pak choy on a plate and top with sauce. Sprinkle black sesame seeds over the top and garnish with fresh coriander.

46

Seared Halibut with Basil Pea Puree

Calories	233
Calories from Fat	54
Total Fat	6g (9%)
Saturated Fat	< 1g (4%)
Cholesterol	46mg (16%)
Sodium	303mg (13%)
Total Carbohydrates	10g (1%)
Dietary Fibre	3g (12%)
Protein	34g
Vitamin A	(16%)
Vitamin C	(22%)
Calcium	(9%)
Iron	(13%)

Dr. Tim says...

Halibut has a high percentage of Omega-3 fats (about 2g in a ¼lb/113g serving). It is in the same flat fish family as flounder but that is where the resemblance ends, as they are large fleshy fish that can weigh up to 1000 lbs. Average size for halibut is about 50 to 100 lbs, however, and it is a prized sport fish in the cold waters of the North Atlantic and North Pacific. It is especially good pan roasted, having a clean, white fish flavour.

¼lb/113g Atlantic/Pacific halibut = 125 calories, 3g fat, <1g sat fat, <1g mono fat, 24g protein, 0g carbohydrates, 127mg sodium, 36mg cholesterol

"Peas are one of the best items to keep in your freezer

Chef Tim says...

Peas are one of the best items to keep in your freezer. The frozen are almost as good as fresh and can make the most simple dish elegant. Fresh peas are not one of those vegetables widely available year round. Avoid tinned peas. Not only do they not taste as good as fresh or frozen, they usually contain added salt as well.

¼ lb/113g frozen peas = 87 calories, <1g fat, 0g sat fat, 0g mono fat, 6g protein, 15g carbohydrates, 127mg sodium, 0mg cholesterol

Serves 4

Serving size = ¼ lb/113g fish

The basil pea puree keeps well for about 24–48 hours refrigerated

Easily multiplied by 2

10oz/300g frozen peas
3 Tbl fresh basil
¼ tsp salt
⅛ tsp ground black pepper
4 x ¼lb/113g fresh halibut fillet
1 tsp extra virgin olive oil

Thaw the frozen peas under cool water. Blend with the fresh basil, salt and pepper until smooth. In a medium-size, stainless or enamelled pan, heat on medium, stirring frequently. When hot, reduce the heat to low to keep warm. Preheat oven to 400°F/205°C. Turn the halibut fillets skin side up on a cutting board and lightly cut stripes in the skin about 1 inch apart. Don't cut completely through the skin to the flesh (this is to keep the fillet from curling as the fish cooks). In a large non-stick frying pan, heat the olive oil over high heat. The oil should be very hot – almost smoking. Place the halibut fillets in the hot pan, skin side up. Cook for about 2 minutes, until the flesh is light brown and has a slight crust to it. Turn, and allow to cook for about 1 minute on the skin side and then place in the hot oven. Roast for about 8 more minutes. As the fish nears being done divide the sauce between 4 plates, making a large pool in the bottom of each plate. Top the sauce with the roasted fish and garnish with fresh basil sprigs.

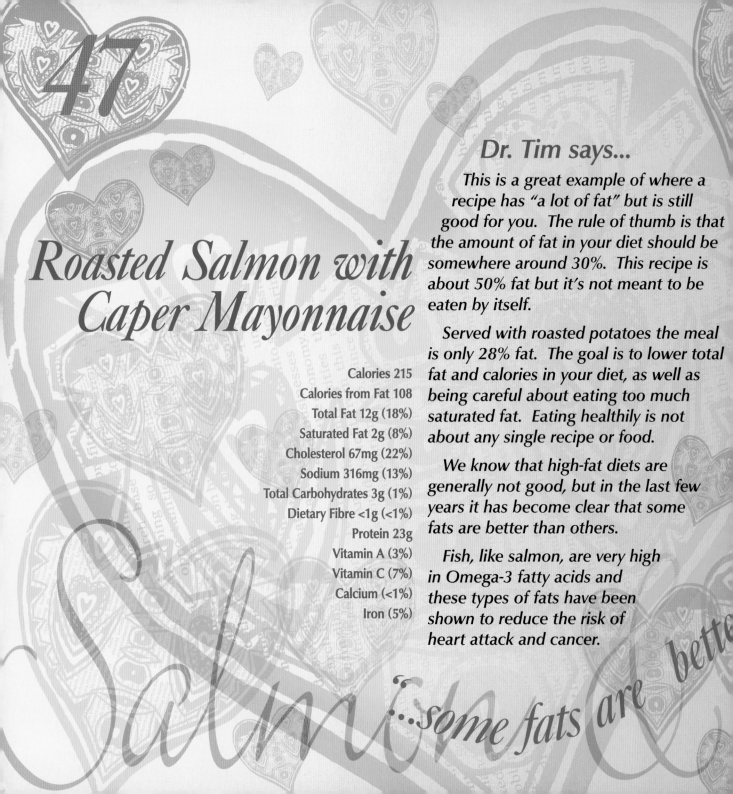

47

Roasted Salmon with Caper Mayonnaise

Calories 215
Calories from Fat 108
Total Fat 12g (18%)
Saturated Fat 2g (8%)
Cholesterol 67mg (22%)
Sodium 316mg (13%)
Total Carbohydrates 3g (1%)
Dietary Fibre <1g (<1%)
Protein 23g
Vitamin A (3%)
Vitamin C (7%)
Calcium (<1%)
Iron (5%)

Dr. Tim says...

This is a great example of where a recipe has "a lot of fat" but is still good for you. The rule of thumb is that the amount of fat in your diet should be somewhere around 30%. This recipe is about 50% fat but it's not meant to be eaten by itself.

Served with roasted potatoes the meal is only 28% fat. The goal is to lower total fat and calories in your diet, as well as being careful about eating too much saturated fat. Eating healthily is not about any single recipe or food.

We know that high-fat diets are generally not good, but in the last few years it has become clear that some fats are better than others.

Fish, like salmon, are very high in Omega-3 fatty acids and these types of fats have been shown to reduce the risk of heart attack and cancer.

Salmon ...some fats are better

Chef Tim says...

Tarragon is one herb where the dried is almost as good as the fresh. The ratio for any herb is about 1 tsp of dried for every 1 Tbl of fresh. 1 tsp of tarragon will provide a lot of flavour but too much of this anise flavoured herb will result in a bitter tasting dish. This mayonnaise is so versatile it can be made with almost any herb: chives, thyme, basil or even lavender!

han others"

Serves 4
Serving size = ¼ lb/113g salmon and 1½ Tbl mayonnaise
The mayonnaise keeps well for about 3 days in the fridge
The leftover fish makes great sandwiches and keeps in the fridge for a day or so
Easily multiplied by 2, 3 or 4

¼ cup low-fat mayonnaise
2 Tbl fresh curly parsley (finely chopped)
½ tsp dried tarragon
1 Tbl fresh lemon juice
2 Tbl capers
4 x ¼ lb/113g salmon fillets

Mix the mayonnaise, parsley, tarragon, lemon juice and capers and chill for at least an hour. Preheat the grill. Place the salmon fillets on a baking tray or in a large frying pan. Grill for about 5 minutes. Top with 2 Tbl of mayonnaise and return to grill for another 3 minutes for medium-rare, or 7 minutes to cook through.

48

Roasted Salmon and Corn Relish

Calories 401

Calories from Fat 126

Total Fat 14g (22%)

Saturated Fat 2.5g (12.5%)

Cholesterol 65mg (22%)

Sodium 357mg (15%)

Total Carbohydrates 34g (11%)

Dietary Fibre 5g (20%)

Protein 34g

Vitamin A (59%)

Vitamin C (77%)

Calcium (4%)

Iron (10%)

Dr. Tim says...

There have been numerous studies that show a reduction of risk in fatal heart attacks when men eat fish. In a study in JAMA, researchers reported similar protection for women, showing that eating fish about once a week reduces the risk for fatal heart attack by at least ⅓. Eating fish more often reduces the risk even further with having fish 2–4 times per week cutting the risk by over 40%. These results were independent of the participants' use of other foods that might also prevent heart disease, such as fibre, or differences in intake of red meat or fruits and vegetables, or lower saturated fat diets.

you have the perfect meal for a dinner party

Chef Tim says...

The amount of calories seems like a lot for a single entrée but this includes the corn relish, which is the starch, and there are plenty of vegetables. For a complete plate, pair this with a simple salad and you have the perfect meal for a dinner party.

Serves 4

Serving size = ¼lb/113g salmon fillet with relish

Leftovers are good and keep a day or so refrigerated

Easily multiplied by 2 or 3

Relish

1 red pepper
1 tsp grapeseed oil
2 cups (2 ears) fresh corn kernels
2 spring onions (sliced)
2 Tbl (1 small) shallot (finely chopped)
1 clove garlic (finely chopped)
1 Tbl fresh thyme leaves
¼ cup dry white wine
1 Tbl fresh lime juice
1 Tbl honey
2 Tbl fresh parsley (finely chopped)
¼ tsp salt

Sauce

1 Tbl grapeseed oil
2 Tbl fresh lime juice
1 Tbl honey
1 Tbl paprika
¼ tsp salt

Fish

4 x ¼lb/113g salmon fillets
2 Tbl fresh coriander (chopped)

Preheat the grill to high. Place the peppers in the oven and char turning about every 3 minutes until black on all sides. Remove and place in a paper bag. After about 10–20 minutes, remove peppers from the bag and the peels will slip off easily.

Once peeled and seeded – cut into ½ inch pieces. Set aside. Slice the white part of the spring onions separately from the green tops. In a large non-stick frying pan, heat the grapeseed oil on medium-high. Add the corn, white part of the spring onions, shallot and garlic and sauté gently until the corn begins to brown. Add the thyme and white wine. Cook on low until the wine evaporates. Stir in the peppers, lime juice, honey, salt, green tops of the spring onions and parsley. Remove from heat. The relish can be made up to 24 hours in advance and reheated gently while the salmon is roasting.

Stir together the 1 Tbl grapeseed oil, lime juice, honey, paprika and salt. The sauce can be made up to 24 hours in advance.

When ready to serve, preheat oven to 400°F/205°C. Line a roasting pan or frying pan with foil. Place the salmon in the middle and top with the sauce. Roast in a hot oven for about 10 minutes. While the salmon is roasting, gently reheat the corn relish. Remove the salmon and top each fillet with a ¼ of the relish and garnish with fresh coriander.

49

Salmon with Parmesan Crust

Calories 345

Calories from Fat 141

Total Fat 16g (26%)

Saturated Fat 5g (20%)

Cholesterol 85mg (28%)

Sodium 382mg (16%)

Total Carbohydrates 15g (5%)

Dietary Fibre <1g (0%)

Protein 30g

Vitamin A (4%)

Vitamin C (0%)

Calcium (20%)

Iron (7%)

Dr. Tim says...

This seemingly simple ingredient, breadcrumbs, has so many different types. It is important to read a recipe carefully and choose the correct breadcrumbs because they are important to the recipe's final texture, what I call, the "mouthfeel". The 2 main types are dry breadcrumbs and fresh breadcrumbs. Dry breadcrumbs usually make for a finer, crisp texture, while fresh have a moist crumbly consistency. Stale bread makes for stale-tasting breadcrumbs. Certainly you can use any type of bread to make your breadcrumbs – whole wheat, French, sourdough, rye or even cinnamon raisin. Keep in mind that breads vary widely in the amount of fat and calories, and ready-made breadcrumbs are vastly inferior to homemade.

Chef Tim says...

In taste tests wild salmon has repeatedly been shown to be preferred over farm-raised salmon. This is felt to be partly due to the higher fat content of wild salmon. Some salmon farmers do claim to feed their salmon diets that help enhance Omega-3 fats. While this may be true, the flavour of farmed salmon is much milder and has less of a true fish taste.

Where and how a wild salmon is caught is also a factor. As the salmon migrate into streams they use up a lot of the fat stores, and with the decline in fat there is a change in flavour. The most coveted fish are caught on trap lines in the ocean. There is less chance of bruising than when the fish is harvested in trolling nets.

Serves 4
Serving size = ¼lb/113g salmon fillet
The breadcrumbs will keep for 24 hours if tightly sealed, beyond that, eat immediately
Easily multiplied by 2 or 3

¼lb/113g fresh French bread
2oz/60g Parmigiano-Reggiano Parmesan cheese (grated)
1 clove garlic (finely chopped)
2 Tbl fresh basil (chiffonade)
2 tsp extra virgin olive oil
1 Tbl balsamic vinegar
4 x ¼lb/113g salmon fillets (no more than ½ in thick)
spray olive oil

Crumb the bread finely. Add the Parmesan, garlic, basil, olive oil and vinegar and process until the mixture is well combined. This will make a moist breadcrumb mixture.

Preheat the oven to 450°F/230°C. Remove the middle rack. Leave a non-stick frying pan in the oven on the lowest possible rack for at least 10 minutes.

Place the salmon fillets on a cutting board skin-side down and pat the breadcrumb mixture onto the top of each fillet. Remove the frying pan from the oven and lightly spray with oil. Transfer the salmon fillets (skin-side down) to the pan and return to the oven. Cook for 6 minutes for rare. Then grill until the crust is golden brown (about 3–5 more minutes).

50

Seared Tuna Steak with Sake-Wasabi Sauce

Calories 222

Calories from Fat 36

Total Fat 4g (6%)

Saturated Fat <1g (0%)

Cholesterol 51mg (17%)

Sodium 388mg (16%)

Total Carbohydrates 19g (7%)

Dietary Fibre 0g (0%)

Protein 27g

Vitamin A (2%)

Vitamin C (10%)

Calcium (3%)

Iron (7%)

Dr. Tim says...

Below are the approximate amounts of Omega-3 fats per 120g serving (120g of fish/meat is about the size of a deck of cards and is just over $\frac{1}{4}$lb)

fresh Atlantic salmon   2,400mg

smoked salmon   2,000mg

canned salmon   1,000mg

sardines   3,000mg

snapper   550mg

fresh rainbow trout   600mg

fresh tuna   1,200mg

canned tuna   290mg

shark   500mg

orange roughey   140mg

crayfish   300mg

oysters (12)   1,000mg

shrimp   200mg

blue mussel   500mg

squid/scallop/calamari 400mg

halibut   2,000mg

makes for a rich and luxurious dish

Chef Tim says...

Searing any meat, like this tuna, makes for a rich and luxurious dish and is a healthy cooking technique. Make sure that the pan is very hot and add the meat carefully, so as to not splash the hot oil.

Serves 4

Serving size = ¼lb/113g tuna steak

Refrigerated leftovers make great sandwiches or salads

Easily multiplied by 2 but requires two large pans

1 Tbl soy sauce
2 Tbl sake (Japanese rice wine)
1 Tbl freshly squeezed lime juice
1Tbl honey
2 tsp wasabi paste
4 x ¼lb/113g tuna steaks (about 1½ inch thick)
fresh ground black pepper
2 tsp dark sesame oil
4 spring onions (sliced)

Mix the sake, soy sauce, lime juice, honey and wasabi paste together in a bowl until the wasabi is completely dissolved.

This can be done a day in advance and refrigerated. Rinse the tuna steaks and pat dry. Liberally sprinkle one side with pepper.

Place the sake sauce in a small, stainless steel or enamelled pan and heat over a low heat. Do not allow the sauce to boil. Set the oven to warm serving plates. Heat the sesame oil in a large non-stick frying pan until almost smoking. Add the tuna steaks, seasoned side down. Cook over medium-high heat until well seared and turn. Rare tuna will take about 4–5 minutes per side.

When the tuna is done, remove the plates from the oven and divide the sauce equally between them, mound a serving of rice in the centre of the sauce and place the tuna on top. Garnish by sprinkling the chopped spring onions over the fish and serve.

51

Thai Coconut Shrimp

Calories 332
Calories from Fat 99
Total Fat 11g (17%)
Saturated Fat 6g (30%)
Cholesterol 28mg (9%)
Sodium 367mg (15%)
Total Carbohydrates 37g (12%)
Dietary Fibre 2g (5%)
Protein 18g
Vitamin A (6%)
Vitamin C (2%)
Calcium (23%)
Iron (13%)

Dr. Tim says...

Soy sauce is one of the world's oldest condiments and is made by fermenting soybeans with roasted wheat (and sometimes barley). Tamari is the gluten-free version. It can add a lot of flavour but it can also add a ton of salt – enough that people who are salt-sensitive or on restricted sodium diets can get into trouble. Traditional soy sauce has about 1100mg of sodium per tablespoon (give or take a 100mg). That's the equivalent to half a teaspoon of salt. Fortunately, there are excellent quality lower sodium soy sauces on the market, with almost no difference in flavour but half the sodium.

Chef Tim says...

Grill pans let you simulate outdoor grilling in the oven. Grill pans are generally larger – about 12–14 inches round or square. They are made with parallel ridges in the bottom, set about ¾ inch apart. This forms a grill-like surface and placing meat or fish (or even veggies) on the superheated pan will mark the food with grill stripes. Fat also drains away to some extent, as with a grill.

Serves 4
Serving size = ¼ lb/113g shrimp
Leftovers are great for sandwiches and keep well if refrigerated for up to 36 hours
Easily multiplied by 2, 3 or 4

Peanut Sauce

4 Tbl low-fat peanut butter
4 Tbl chicken stock
2 Tbl low-fat coconut milk
1 tsp low-sodium soy sauce
1 tsp rice vinegar
1 tsp Tabasco

Marinade

½ cup low-fat coconut milk
2 cloves garlic (finely chopped)
2 Tbl fresh lime juice
1 Tbl fresh ginger (peeled & finely chopped)
1 Tbl low-sodium soy sauce
2 tsp hoisin sauce
1 Tbl maple syrup
1 cup Thai basil (finely chopped)
1lb/454g shrimp (peeled and deveined)
Coconut Rice – see next recipe

Combine the ingredients for the peanut sauce in a small bowl. Whisk until smooth and set aside.

Blend the coconut milk, garlic, lime juice, ginger, low-sodium soy sauce, hoisin sauce, maple syrup and Thai basil until smooth.

Using two medium-sized wooden skewers, assemble small kebabs of shrimp. The amount of shrimp on each kebab will be determined by the size of shrimp that is used. For medium-sized shrimp, this will be about 4 shrimp per kebab for a total of 16 kebabs. Put the shrimp in the bottom of an oblong dish and add the marinade. Cover tightly with plastic wrap and place in the refrigerator for at least 3 hours (overnight is fine). When ready to cook, preheat the oven to 400°F/200°C. Place a grill pan in the oven and let heat for at least 10 minutes. When hot, add the marinated shrimp skewers. As they sear on one side, top the other with about half of the marinade. The shrimp will grill fast and should be turned after about 3 minutes. Spread the remaining marinade over the top of the shrimp and grill for another 4–5 minutes. Serve over Coconut Rice with 2 Tbl of the peanut sauce.

1 Tbl low-sodium soy sauce = 10 calories, 0g fat, 0g sat fat, 0g mono fat, 2g protein, 1g carbohydrates, 590mg sodium, 0mg cholesterol

1 Tbl soy sauce = 10 calories, 0g fat, 0g sat fat, 0g mono fat, 1g protein, 2g carbohydrates, 1029mg sodium, 0mg cholesterol.

52

Coconut Rice

Calories 203
Calories from Fat 27
Total Fat 3g (5%)
Saturated Fat 3g (15%)
Cholesterol 0mg (0%)
Sodium 293mg (12%)
Total Carbohydrates 37g (12%)
Dietary Fibre <1g (2%)
Protein 3g
Vitamin A (0%)
Vitamin C (0%)
Calcium (1%)
Iron (11%)

Dr. Tim says...

There is quite a difference between regular coconut milk, at 45g of fat per cup, and the low-fat version, at about 12g of fat per cup. In both regular and low-fat coconut milk most of the fat is highly saturated, so always try to use coconut milk sparingly.

Chef Tim says...

Never stir rice because stirring breaks down the starches on the outer layer and turns the rice to a gooey paste. Simply place the rice in the boiling liquid, stir once and cover. Leave it alone to simmer until the water has evaporated.

Serves 2
Serving size = ½ cup rice
The rice doesn't keep well
Easily multiplied by 2, 3 or 4

½ cup tinned unsweetened low-fat coconut milk
¾ cup water
¼ tsp salt
½ cup jasmine rice

Prior to opening the tin of coconut milk, shake very well. In a medium pan heat the coconut milk, water and salt. When the liquid boils, stir in the jasmine rice. Reduce heat to medium-low and simmer, covered, for about 15 minutes. Do not boil away all of the liquid and do not stir the rice. When a very small amount of liquid remains, remove the pan from the burner and let it stand, covered, for 5 minutes before serving.

53

Yellow Pepper & White Asparagus Soft Tacos

Calories 345
Calories from Fat 117
Total Fat 13g (20%)
Saturated Fat 5g (25%)
Cholesterol 20mg (7%)
Sodium 709mg (30%)
Total Carbohydrates 41g (14%)
Dietary Fibre 5g (20%)
Protein 15g
Vitamin A (31%)
Vitamin C (300%)
Calcium (29%)
Iron (18%)

Dr. Tim says...

Lycopenes are the antioxidant chemical that is the major red pigment in fruits and vegetables. In a recent study of over 45,000 men, researchers at Harvard University found that eating foods containing high amounts of lycopene reduced the risk of prostate cancer by about 35%. There are also studies that show lycopenes have a beneficial effect on LDL (bad cholesterol), but none that prove a correlation between eating foods high in lycopenes and a lowered risk of heart disease.

Tomatoes are one of the best sources of lycopenes and cooking them helps release the antioxidant. A medium tomato has about 3.5mg of lycopene, while tomato sauce almost 20mg in a half a cup, and tomato soup about 25mg in a cup. Other fruits and vegetables that have red pigment, like watermelon and grapefruit, are good sources of lycopene as well. There is so much discussion about antioxidants and here's another one that may have some benefit. The bottom line is that eating good food is good for you.

Chef Tim says...

Asparagus is actually a member of the lily family and is a perennial, with plants living up to ten years. Most people think that thinner stalks are those harvested earlier in the year but the thickness indicates the age of the plant, with the thicker stems coming from older plants. White asparagus is increasingly available, as is the purple variety.

Asparagus doesn't keep well but will stay fresher in the refrigerator by cutting the stalks near the bottom and placing them upright in water. Older, thicker stalks can be woody, and peeling the skin at the base will remove the tough layer. Peeled asparagus poaches much faster.

¼lb/113g asparagus = 26 calories, 0g fat, 0g sat fat, 0g mono fat, 3g protein, 5g carbohydrates, 2mg sodium, 0mg cholesterol

Serves 2
Serving size = 1 soft taco
Eat immediately
Easily multiplied by 2, 3 or 4

1 tsp grapeseed oil
1 clove garlic (finely chopped)
½ medium white onion (diced)
½ large yellow pepper (diced)
½ medium hot chilli (finely chopped)
1 Tbl tomato paste
¼ cup low-calorie beer
¼ cup chicken stock
fresh ground black pepper to taste
6 spears white asparagus (blanched)
2 low-fat flour tortillas
¼ medium avocado (sliced)
2oz/60g low-fat cheese (shredded)
½ cup fresh coriander
1 small tomato (seeded and cut into strips)

Heat the grapeseed oil on medium heat in a frying pan. Add the garlic. Cook slowly to prevent it browning or it will turn bitter. After about 2 minutes add the onions. Cook over medium heat and when the onions begin to soften add the yellow pepper. Cook for about 2–4 minutes, tossing frequently. Add the chilli pepper and tomato paste and stir.

After about 1 minute add the beer, chicken stock and pepper. Cook over medium heat, tossing frequently until about ½ the liquid has gone. Add the asparagus spears. Continue tossing until almost all of the liquid has gone. Warm both tortillas for about 1 minute in a medium-sized frying pan and place each one on a plate. Divide the sliced avocado between the 2 tortillas, placing it down the centre of each, then top with the heated vegetables, cheese, coriander and tomato. Roll into a tube and eat.

> *The most remarkable thing about my mother is that for thirty years she served the family nothing but leftovers. The original meal has never been found*

Calvin Trillin
Author

sweets

54

Cheesecake

Calories 146
Calories from Fat 63
Total Fat 7g (11%)
Saturated Fat 3g (15%)
Sodium 473mg (20%)
Total Carbohydrates 11g (8%)
Dietary Fibre <1g (<1%)
Protein 9g

Dr. Tim says...

Dessert is an essential part of a healthy diet. There are two keys to making sure that you are getting the most out of your sweets. The first is to eat dessert as an occasional treat.

Most desserts are simply added calories. The second rule of thumb is to look for desserts that are less than 200 calories and save the higher calorie, really rich desserts, for very special occasions.

Chef Tim says...

Cottage cheese is simply the step before cheese is allowed to solidify and the result is very high moisture curds. It is low in fat, with the whole milk version being 2g fat per oz. Low-fat cottage cheese is 1g of fat per oz.

½ cup cottage cheese = 120 calories, 5g fat, 3g sat fat, 0g mono fat, 13g protein, 5g carbohydrates, 400mg sodium, 25mg cholesterol

½ cup low-fat cottage cheese = 90 calories, 2.5g fat, 1.5g sat fat, 0g mono fat, 13g protein, 4g carbohydrates, 389mg sodium, 15mg cholesterol

½ cup fat-free cottage cheese = 80 calories, 0g fat, 0g sat fat, 0g mono fat, 13g protein, 6g carbohydrates, 439mg sodium, 5mg cholesterol

Serves 12
Serving size = ¹⁄₁₂ of the cheesecake
Keeps refrigerated for a couple of days but the fresher the better
Do not multiply

Crust

8 light digestive biscuits
1 Tbl honey
1 Tbl rapeseed oil

Filling

1lb/450g Philadelphia Extra Light Cream Cheese
1 cup 1% cottage cheese
½ cup soured cream
1 cup Splenda
1 tsp pure vanilla extract
¼ cup fresh lemon juice
1 large egg white
1 large egg
¼ tsp salt
3 egg whites
pinch Cream of Tartar

Preheat the oven to 300°F/150°C. Line a spring clip pan with tin foil by removing the pan bottom and placing it on top of two 18 inch square sheets of foil. Fold the edges in. Slip the sides of the pan down over the foil. Close the clip and then press the foil against the inside of the sides of the pan. The result will be the foil outside the pan on the bottom and inside the pan on the sides.

Crumb the biscuits. Combine with honey and oil until well blended. Press the crumb mixture into the bottom of the spring clip pan. Place the pan in the oven and cook for 15 minutes. Remove from the oven to cool.

While the crust is cooling, blend the cheeses, sour cream, Splenda, vanilla extract, lemon juice, egg white, egg and salt until a smooth batter. Whisk the 3 remaining egg whites with the Cream of Tartar until they form stiff peaks and fold gently into the batter. Pour into the crumb-lined pan.

Place the pan in a further, larger pan of water. This creates a heated water bath, or bain marie, and bake for one hour. Turn off the oven and remove the water bath from the oven. Return just the cheesecake (without the water bath) to the warm oven and allow to sit for 2 hours in the oven as it cools. Chill for at least 4 hours before serving.

55

Chocolate Sauce

Calories 45

Calories from Fat 0

Total Fat <1g (5%)

Saturated Fat <1g (2%)

Cholesterol 0mg (0%)

Sodium 82mg (3%)

Total Carbohydrates 10g (6%)

Dietary Fibre 2g

Protein 2g

Vitamin A (<1%)

Vitamin C (<1%)

Calcium (2%)

Iron (5%)

Dr. Tim says...

Chocolate is good for you!

Or at least, not bad for you as most people think. Yes it contains fat, but it's a type of fat that doesn't cause a rise in blood cholesterol levels. The fat is from a plant, not an animal, so it contains the beneficial substances of foods of plant origin. It also has small amounts of copper, zinc, iron and magnesium along with polyphenols, which have proven health benefits.

Both cocoa powder and chocolate are derived from a bean that's high in flavonoids (a known antioxidant) and these can reduce the risk of heart disease.

Chocolate is good for you! Or at least, not bad for you...

Chef Tim says...

Strong coffee works well in dessert recipes that call for chocolate by enhancing the chocolate flavour. It's also worth trying the no-calorie sweetener Splenda.

Splenda has most of the properties of sugar and will work in most recipes. The test version of this, made with Splenda instead of granulated sugar, saved about 25 calories per serving.

It wasn't a total failure but it just didn't have the quality of the sauce made with granulated sugar.

Certainly, if you are diabetic using Splenda is a great substitute for sauces like this.

Serves 8
Serving size = 2 Tbl
Keeps well for about a week in the fridge
Easily multiplied by 2

½ cup Dutch process cocoa
¼ cup granulated sugar
¼ cup strong coffee
½ cup non-fat milk
1 tsp pure vanilla extract
¼ tsp salt
1 Tbl all purpose flour

Heat the cocoa, granulated sugar, coffee, milk, vanilla extract and salt, in a non-reactive pan over medium heat. Whisk constantly until smooth.

Add the flour and whisk for another minute and remove from heat. Whisk about every 2 minutes for 20 minutes, while cooling.

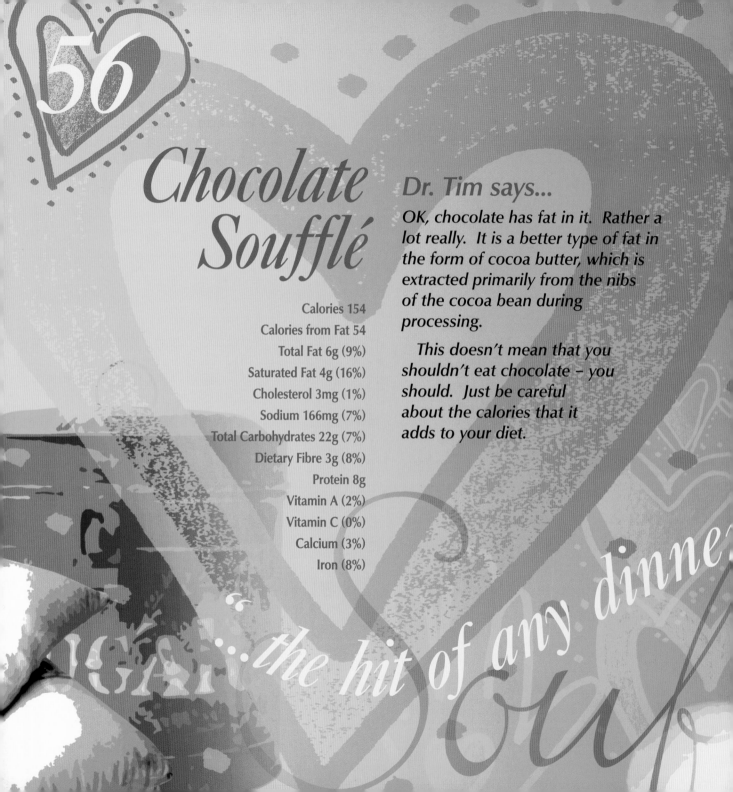

56

Chocolate Soufflé

Calories 154

Calories from Fat 54

Total Fat 6g (9%)

Saturated Fat 4g (16%)

Cholesterol 3mg (1%)

Sodium 166mg (7%)

Total Carbohydrates 22g (7%)

Dietary Fibre 3g (8%)

Protein 8g

Vitamin A (2%)

Vitamin C (0%)

Calcium (3%)

Iron (8%)

Dr. Tim says...

OK, chocolate has fat in it. Rather a lot really. It is a better type of fat in the form of cocoa butter, which is extracted primarily from the nibs of the cocoa bean during processing.

This doesn't mean that you shouldn't eat chocolate – you should. Just be careful about the calories that it adds to your diet.

...the hit of any dinner

Chef Tim says...

Use this basic recipe to make any kind of soufflé. The recipe is simple – sauce and egg whites. Almost any fruit can end up as a dessert that will be the hit of any dinner party. Once soufflé becomes a regular on your table, think about investing in a copper bowl. The chemical reaction that takes place between the protein in the egg and the copper in the bowl, helps to stiffen the whites.

If you don't have a copper bowl use a pinch of Cream of Tartar to help mimic this reaction.

party

Serves 2 (makes 2 soufflés)
Serving Size = 1 soufflé
There are no leftovers
Easily multiplied by 2 but care must be taken with whipping 6 egg whites

½ tsp unsalted butter
1 tsp granulated sugar
3 large egg whites
⅛ tsp Cream of Tartar
1oz/28g bittersweet chocolate (grated)
¼ cup chocolate sauce (previous recipe)

Preheat oven to 400°F/205°C. Butter each soufflé dish with about ½ tsp butter and add ¼ tsp granulated sugar to each dish, tapping to coat the sides well. Whisk the egg whites together with the Cream of Tartar until stiff peaks form. Fold in the grated chocolate carefully. Fold in ¼ cup of the chocolate sauce. Spoon into the soufflé dishes and bake for 12–15 minutes. Serve quickly with a light sprinkle of powdered sugar over the top of each soufflé.

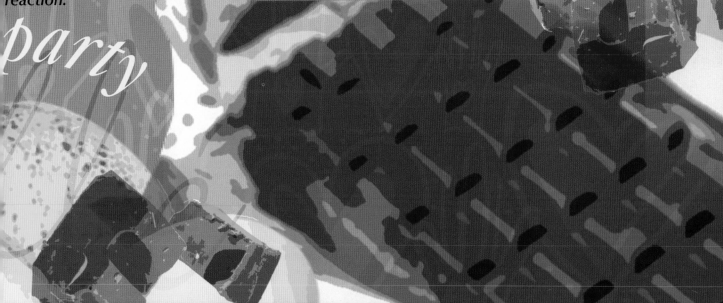

57

Banoffee Pie

Calories 215

Calories from Fat 63

Total Fat 7g (11%)

Saturated Fat 3g (15%)

Sodium 322mg (13%)

Total Carbohydrates–
32g (11%)

Dietary Fibre 1g (4%)

Protein 7g

Dr. Tim says...

Regular cream cheese is made with milk that contains about 35% butterfat. In practical terms this works out to about 14g of fat in 1oz of regular cream cheese and only 7g in the light version. Extra light cream cheese can be used in place of regular cream cheese in most recipes, and will save a lot of fat and calories in your desserts. Because it has a higher moisture content, the amount of liquid may need to be reduced in some recipes, especially when baking.

30g extra light cream cheese = 30 calories, 1.5g fat, 1g sat fat, 3g protein, 3g carbohydrates, 200mg sodium

Chef Tim says...

When you are making the caramel it is important to pay attention to it.

Don't try to do anything else because the sugar will turn darker and burn quickly. The only solution if this happens is to start again.

It may take some practise but the reward is a real Banoffee pie that has only 215 calories.

Serves 8
Serving Size = ⅛ pie
Keeps for 48 hours at most without bananas or whipped cream
Does not multiply

Crust

8 light digestive biscuits
1 Tbl honey
1 Tbl rapeseed oil

Filling

5oz/150ml light evaporated milk
2 Tbl water
½ cup granulated sugar
½ cup Splenda
½lb/225g Philadelphia Extra Light Cream Cheese
1 banana
1 batch whipped cream (see recipe 61)
1 tsp instant coffee granules

Place the can of evaporated milk in a large pot filled with water. Heat the water to a slow boil for 5 hours being careful to keep the water from boiling away. Remove and let cool (this can be done up to a week in advance).

Preheat the oven to 300°F/150°C. Crumb the digestive biscuits and then stir in the honey and rapeseed oil until well blended. Press into a 9 inch non-stick pie pan and place in the oven and cook for 15 minutes. Remove and let cool.

Place the evaporated milk in a small non-reactive saucepan over medium heat but do not allow it to boil. Place the water and granulated sugar in a high-sided non-reactive saucepan. Heat over high heat swirling frequently. As the sugar dissolves and boils, watch the pan carefully, continuing to swirl. The syrup will thicken and begin to turn a golden colour. As it cooks the colour will darken. Continue to swirl. As soon as there is a slight smoke remove from the heat, swirling continuously. As the syrup cools it will thicken and continue to darken. When it is the consistency of honey, add the hot evaporated milk, whisking continuously. The milk will foam in the hot pan and as it cools it will thicken slightly.

Add Splenda and the cream cheese and stir it into the caramelized milk until smooth. Add to the piecrust and chill for at least 3 hours.

When ready to serve slice the banana, arranging the slices to cover the top of the pie. Whisk the instant coffee granules into Recipe 61 and top the pie with whipped cream.

the perfect dessert to serve your guests

Custard Cream

Calories 57

Calories from Fat 27

Total Fat 3g (5%)

Saturated Fat 1g (4%)

Cholesterol 58mg (19%)

Sodium 34mg (1%)

Total Carbohydrates 5g (2%)

Dietary Fibre 0g (0%)

Protein 3g

Vitamin A (5%)

Vitamin C (1%)

Calcium (9%)

Iron (1%)

Dr. Tim says...

This custard is the perfect dessert to serve your guests at a dinner party. A bit over some fresh fruit is the perfect end to any meal and will have only about 100 calories. It will be so rich they won't even know that it's good for them.

Chef Tim says...

I like to use a vanilla bean in this recipe, by splitting it open and heating it slowly with the milk, but you don't always have the time. Recipes that call for pure vanilla extract deserve just that.

Artificial vanilla has the aroma but not the flavour of pure vanilla extract. The real stuff is more expensive but, as with everything you cook, quality ingredients make the right dish.

Serves 8
Serving Size = ¼ cup custard
Keeps fairly well for about
48 hours
Do not multiply

2 cups semi-skimmed milk
2 Tbl arrowroot flour
2 large egg yolks
2 tsp unsalted butter
3 Tbl Splenda
1½ tsp pure vanilla extract

Place 1¾ cups of the milk in a non-reactive saucepan and heat over medium heat. While it is heating combine the other ¼ cup of milk with the arrowroot, egg yolks, butter, Splenda and vanilla extract, whisking well until smooth.

When the milk is hot but not boiling, remove about a ¼ cup and combine with the milk/arrowroot/egg mixture. Whisk well and then place this into the pan of milk. Heat while stirring continuously. As the sauce begins to thicken to the consistency of soured cream, remove from the heat and keep whisking frequently until it is warm. Chill at least 3 hours. Serve over fruit or other dessert.

quality ingredients make the right dish

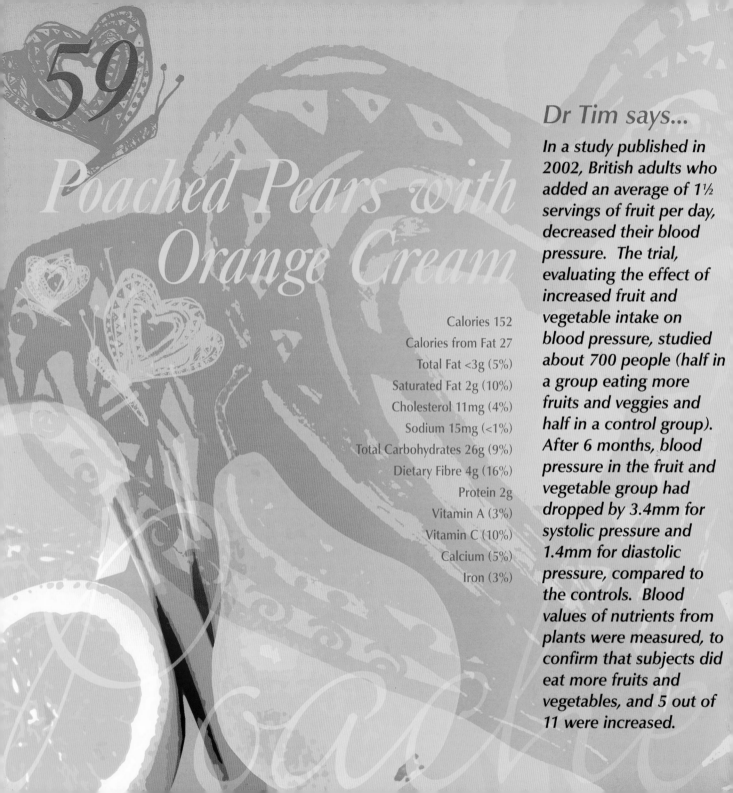

59

Poached Pears with Orange Cream

Calories 152

Calories from Fat 27

Total Fat <3g (5%)

Saturated Fat 2g (10%)

Cholesterol 11mg (4%)

Sodium 15mg (<1%)

Total Carbohydrates 26g (9%)

Dietary Fibre 4g (16%)

Protein 2g

Vitamin A (3%)

Vitamin C (10%)

Calcium (5%)

Iron (3%)

Dr Tim says...

In a study published in 2002, British adults who added an average of 1½ servings of fruit per day, decreased their blood pressure. The trial, evaluating the effect of increased fruit and vegetable intake on blood pressure, studied about 700 people (half in a group eating more fruits and veggies and half in a control group). After 6 months, blood pressure in the fruit and vegetable group had dropped by 3.4mm for systolic pressure and 1.4mm for diastolic pressure, compared to the controls. Blood values of nutrients from plants were measured, to confirm that subjects did eat more fruits and vegetables, and 5 out of 11 were increased.

Chef Tim says...

Good quality Anjou pears are full of sweet and succulent juice. They are short and squat without the classic tapered neck. They are slightly soft and, because of this, are not a great choice for cooking. Bartlett pears are a little soft and grainy for cooking but are excellent pears for eating raw.

Winter pears such as Bosc and Conference pears have a tartness that cuts through the sweet pear flavour. Bosc are pear shaped and somewhat firmer. That firm texture lends itself well to cooking and the true pear shape is perfect for presentation.

1 pear = 98 calories, 0g fat, 0g sat fat, 0g mono fat, <1g protein, 25g carbohydrates, 0mg sodium, 0mg cholesterol

Serves 4
Serving size = 1 pear & 2 Tbl sauce
Keeps well for about a week
Easily multiplied by 2 or 3 using a larger pot

Pears

1½ cups Splenda
½ cinnamon stick
6 whole cloves
2 Tbl pure vanilla extract
2 Tbl fresh grated lemon zest
6 cups water
4 pears (peeled)

Sauce

¼ cup sour cream
¼ cup semi-skimmed milk
1 tsp fresh grated orange peel
1 Tbl Splenda
2 Tbl Grand Marnier

Combine the water, Splenda, cinnamon, vanilla, cloves and lemon zest in a medium non-reactive saucepan.

Heat over medium-high heat until the water is shivering but not boiling. Cut a thin slice from the bottom of each peeled pear so that it will sit upright. Reduce the heat to medium-low, add the pears and poach them for 30 minutes. Let the pears cool in the poaching water and then place in the refrigerator until cold.

While the fruit is cooling, mix together the sour cream, milk, orange peel, Splenda and Grand Marnier. Chill.

Serve each pear on a plate sitting upright and place a dollop of orange cream to the side. Garnish with orange slices.

60

Cr ème Brûlée

Calories 184

Calories from Fat 45

Total Fat 5g (8%)

Saturated Fat 2g (10%)

Cholesterol 119mg (40%)

Sodium 173mg (7%)

Total Carbohydrates 23g (8%)

Dietary Fibre 0g (0%)

Protein 12g

Vitamin A (8%)

Vitamin C (4%)

Calcium (25%)

Iron (55%)

Dr. Tim says...

Sugar melts at about 320°F/160ºC and will turn to a clear liquid at that temperature. As the heat increases, the sugar will turn golden brown. Towards 350°F/175ºC it will darken. When the liquid cools, it turns to a crisp glaze.

Using a blowtorch lets the sugar melt quickly, while the custard remains cool.

A blowtorch doesn't cost much. Not bad for a bit of heaven any time you like...

Chef Tim says...

Custards require gentle heating of eggs and milk. Using the dry milk powder as an enhancement for the milk creates a richer dessert. Try lavender or rosemary leaves, orange peel or mocha, for interesting variations.

Start with about a teaspoon of flavouring in this recipe and adjust for taste.

you like...

Serves 4
Serving size = 1 custard
The custards keep well for a few days
Wrap tightly
Easily multiplied by 2

2 cups semi-skimmed milk
½ cup non-fat dry milk powder
1 tsp pure vanilla extract
6 Tbl Splenda
⅛ tsp salt
2 large egg yolks
8 tsp granulated sugar

In a non-reactive pan, heat semi-skimmed milk, dry milk powder and vanilla extract on medium heat until the mixture reaches 180°F/90ºC, just below boiling. Remove from the heat and allow to cool at least a few hours, preferably overnight in the refrigerator.

Preheat the oven to 300°F/150°C. Fill a roasting pan with water to a level that will be about ¾ of the way up a 1-cup ramekin. This is the water bath. It is best to test this by placing all the ramekins in the water bath to make sure it is not overfilled. Heat the bath in the oven for about 20 minutes.

Cream the Splenda, egg yolks and salt until smooth. Strain the milk mixture through a fine sieve, into the egg mixture. Whisk. Divide the milk/egg mixture between 4 1-cup ramekins. Place the ramekins in the water bath in the oven and cook for 60 minutes. Remove the roasting pan from the oven, taking care not to slop the water from the bath into the ramekins. Allow the custard to cool for 30 minutes, while still in the water bath. Cover each custard with cling film and chill overnight. Place 2 tsp of sugar on the top of each custard. Using a blowtorch, melt the sugar by carefully aiming the tip of the flame at the surface of the sugar. Tilt and rotate the ramekin so that the melted sugar covers the surface of the custard. Serve.

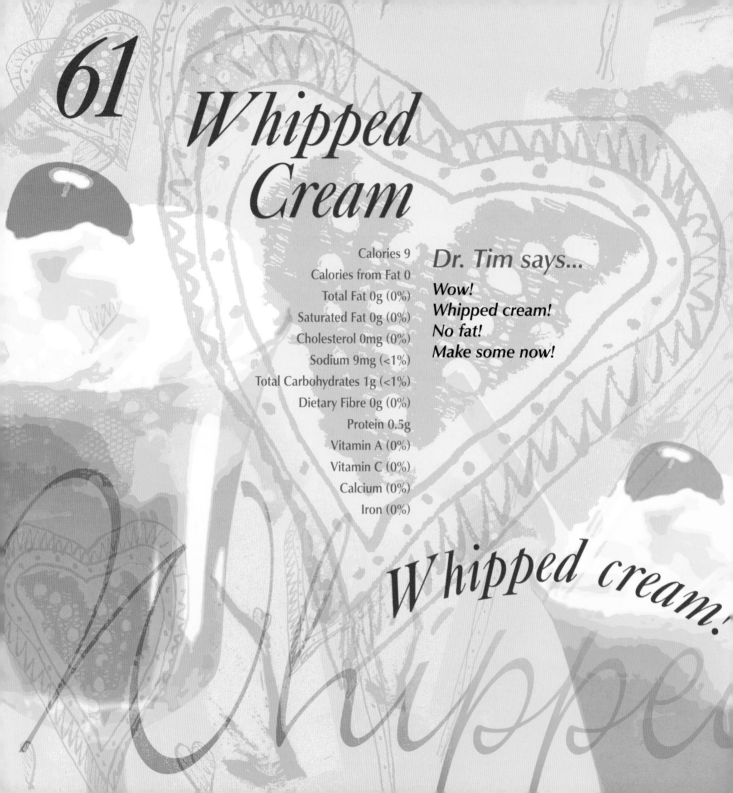

61 *Whipped Cream*

Calories 9
Calories from Fat 0
Total Fat 0g (0%)
Saturated Fat 0g (0%)
Cholesterol 0mg (0%)
Sodium 9mg (<1%)
Total Carbohydrates 1g (<1%)
Dietary Fibre 0g (0%)
Protein 0.5g
Vitamin A (0%)
Vitamin C (0%)
Calcium (0%)
Iron (0%)

Dr. Tim says...

Wow!
Whipped cream!
No fat!
Make some now!

Whipped cream!

Chef Tim says...

This is a great technique but as with regular whipped cream it is not very stable and has to be used within about 45 minutes of being made.

Keep it as cold as possible. It works well with light evaporated milk but this gives it a more caramelized flavour.

Serves 12
Serving Size = ⅓ cup
(makes 4 cups)
This recipe doesn't keep well
The whipped cream can be made up to 45 minutes in advance but must be kept very cold
Whisk lightly before serving
This recipe is not easily multiplied

1 envelope/7g unflavoured gelatine
¼ cup cold water
1½ cups skimmed milk
¼ cup Splenda
1 tsp pure vanilla extract

In a small bowl, sprinkle the envelope of unflavoured gelatine over the cold water and let stand until the gelatine absorbs the water. In a medium saucepan over medium-low heat, scald the milk. Remove from the heat and add it to the gelatine, whisking until the gelatine dissolves. Stir in the Splenda and vanilla extract.

Refrigerate, stirring every 10 minutes, until very cold (about 1½ hours), then place in a large bowl of ice water for 30 minutes and let it stand, whisking often. Using a handheld mixer, set at high-speed, beat until the mixture is thick and fluffy.

Make some now!

DR TIM HARLAN

Dr. Tim Harlan is a practising physician
in Virginia USA. As a younger man he was chef
and owner of a small French bistro.
Working in the catering industry throughout his
medical studies Dr. Tim combined his love of
food and knowledge of medicine to create the
personae of Dr Gourmet.

Helping people eat well and still eat healthily,
Dr. Tim has developed a large TV and Internet
following. In 2002 his TV contribution to diet and
public health awareness won him an Emmy®.

Photograph © 2004 Gary Gruby

More information can be found at:
http://www.drgourmet.com